Manned
Space
Flight

Max Faget

Coordinating Editor:
James V. Bernardo, Director
Educational Programs and Services
National Aeronautics and Space Administration

Holt, Rinehart and Winston, Inc., New York

Max Faget is the Assistant Director for Engineering and Development at the Manned Spacecraft Center, National Aeronautics and Space Administration.

Born in British Honduras, Mr. Faget received his higher education in California and Louisiana. After earning a degree in Mechanical Engineering from Louisiana State University, he joined the staff of the Langley Research Center, in Hampton, Virginia. There he worked in the Pilotless Aircraft Research Division and later became head of the Performance Aerodynamics Branch. He was one of the original group of 35, known as the Space Task Group, assigned as a nucleus for the Manned Spacecraft Center.

He conceived and proposed the development of a one-man spacecraft, later used in Project Mercury. He also was a member of the Polaris Missile Steering Task Group and greatly influenced the design of that Navy missile.

Mr. Faget won the Arthur S. Fleming Award for outstanding Federal Service; the NASA medal for Outstanding Leadership; and the Golden Plate Award presented by the Academy of Achievement. He is a member of several professional societies, has authored and co-authored numerous technical papers, and is the co-author of the textbook, "Engineering Design and Operation of Spacecraft."

Original drawings: Versatron Corporation

Preface

The design, construction and successful operation of manned spacecraft represents one of the great engineering accomplishments of recent years. The natural difficulties that must be overcome in making space flight safe and reliable are so great that every possible advantage must be taken of modern science and technology.

It is the purpose of this short book to discuss some of the technical problems facing the builders of manned spacecraft, and to explain the various facets of science which came into play in the engineering solutions of these problems. Since the general intention is to emphasize fundamental concepts, the discussion contains very little technical sophistication. It is hoped, however, that the reader's interest will be excited to the extent that he will delve further into the adventures of the world of space technology.

Contents

1

Spaceflight Missions and Environment

In the past, imaginative men have dreamed of exploring the heavens. Galileo discovered the telescope in 1609, and since that time men have been able to learn much about the stars and planets by observation and by deduction based upon observing the nature of physical phenomena on earth. We know that the Earth and eight other planets rotate about the sun. Our sun and its planets are called the *solar system*. The sun is just one of perhaps 100 billion stars that belong to a system of stars called a *galaxy*. Our galaxy is just one of a very great number of galaxies stretching out as far as men can see with the most powerful telescope. The Earth is nothing more than a tiny bit of matter in this vastness. Yet men will continue to struggle to learn more about the universe and how it came to be created. The launching of instruments into space on tiny spacecraft has greatly enhanced our knowledge of the solar system. The exploration of the moon and some of the nearby planets by men promises to be the greatest adventure in history.

Today's science and technology, however, will not be able to produce a spacecraft that can carry men to distances further than the most immediate planets. Moreover, it is not yet possible to even imagine the principles upon which an interstellar spaceship will be designed and constructed. Yet if one considers the changes brought about during this century in transportation technology, it is not impossible that flight to nearby stars might be practical within several decades. Certainly, when the first airplanes were being flown, one could have said that, based upon the principles employed in those early machines, flight into space would not be possible. And yet, we have flown into space by developing new principles of flight that are in some ways quite unrelated to those used in airplanes.

Learning to Fly in Space

The flights of the American Mercury and Russian Vostok spacecraft were made for the purpose of exploring the concept of flying into space. Since these flights were initial efforts, the purpose of the flights was limited to the basic experience of launching the spacecraft and crew into orbit, having them remain there for a period of time, and then having them return safely to Earth. These flights were made at low altitude with the spacecraft orbiting barely high enough to avoid appreciable drag from the upper fringes of the atmosphere. By keeping the orbital altitude to a minimum, the amount of energy required for launching was minimized, and the flight was made safer, since the difficulty of making a reentry maneuver was also minimized. The main significance of these flights was that they proved that it was practical for man to fly in space. They also provided valuable lessons in design and operation of spacecraft that will provide a sound basis upon which future projects may be planned.

Project Mercury, conducted by the National Aeronautics and Space Administration (NASA), has been successfully completed. The follow-on project to continue the man-in-space portion of NASA's program, is called *Gemini*.

The Gemini project will extend our knowledge and experience in orbital flight. Compared to Mercury, the Gemini spacecraft is sophisticated and able to stay aloft for a longer duration. It may perform maneuvers in space and during reentry. With them, we will investigate rendezvous techniques of one spacecraft with another, and for making landings on the ground at the termination of a space mission. Since the Gemini carries a crew of two, it is practical to have one of the crew leave the spacecraft and float freely in space, protected by his spacesuit, while his companion continues to tend the spacecraft. He is able to return to the spacecraft by pulling himself in on an attached tether, or perhaps, by the use of a small, jet-powered device provided for such extra-vehicular excursions. Although the main purpose of these flights will be to investigate in detail some of the principles of space flight, they will also provide a means for carrying out certain scientific observations from space.

The Manned Orbital Laboratory

The orbital laboratory, or space station, may follow the flights of Gemini. This would be the first use of orbital flight in which the basic purpose will not be to learn more about spacecraft and space flight. The space station will be an experimental laboratory in space where scientific and technical investigators can carry out various observations and experiments for extended periods of time, with sufficient room and equipment to facilitate a great variety of projects. Such a laboratory

Fig. 1-1.   A design concept for a large orbital space station. (NASA)

will weigh several hundred tons and will be furnished to house
two or three dozen people for one or more years. It will be
serviced by ferry spacecraft that will carry men, supplies and
equipment back and forth from earth. The space station will
be made to rotate slowly so that the centrifugal force that is
created will provide an artificial gravity field. It is thought that
such an artificial gravity field will be more convenient to the
crew than weightlessness and may even be necessary from a
physiological standpoint for extended periods in space. However, a portion of the space station near the center will not
rotate, and in this region a zero-gravitation field will exist as
an area for carrying out those experiments that are associated
with this condition. Since the only known way to create a
zero-gravity condition for extended periods of time is with
space flight, this laboratory area on the space station will provide a unique capability for a great number of experiments in
the physical and life science areas, and will also be a valuable
proving ground for engineering and development test work
for future spacecraft components.

There are other features about the space station which make
it valuable. It will be a place for observing the sun, planets
and stars without the interference of the Earth's atmosphere.
It will provide a means by which the environment of space
near the earth may be measured in great detail. It will provide
a platform from which the earth may be observed from the
outside. It will provide a vacuum and cold-temperature environment free from the many limitations that are associated
with vacuum chambers on Earth.

Lunar Exploration

The aspect of space flight most appealing to the imagination
is that it will some day provide the opportunity for travel to
other worlds. The Apollo project, to follow Gemini, has as its
mission the round trip transportation of men to the surface of
the moon. Apollo will therefore be the first application of
space flight for transportation. Certainly, it is a modest effort
in that only two astronauts will be landed on the moon with

sufficient equipment to maintain their presence for a few hours. However, when one considers that the moon is almost 250,000 miles away and that its direction is *up*, some appreciation of the difficulty of the task may be obtained. The orbital altitude of the moon is more than a thousand times greater than the altitude normally used by manned orbital vehicles. The gravitational attraction of the moon must be overcome by a great expenditure of propellants not only during the launching and departure maneuvers, but also during the approach and landing maneuvers. Unlike the Earth, the moon has no atmosphere. Therefore, rocket thrust must be used to dissipate the velocity and overcome the pull of gravity as the moon is approached. Apollo must carry over 30 tons of propellant to the moon to make these various maneuvers.

The moon has been the Earth's companion since the time of their creation. Yet, the moon's surface has been subjected to a different environment. Certainly there have been volcanos as on the earth. However, the period of volcanic activity on the moon may have ceased long ago and the core of the moon may no longer be active. This conjecture is prompted by the fact that the moon is smaller than the Earth. The important thing about the moon's surface, however, is that it has been ruled by the environment of space during the time that the Earth's surface has been undergoing many changes that have masked the clues to its beginning. Thus on the moon we may expect to obtain facts about two things. First, we may establish a better knowledge about the creation of the solar system since some of the features of this process will be better preserved on the moon's surface. Second, we will find a history of the environment of space etched in the surface of the moon, which should be valuable in ascertaining the history of the solar system.

Although each Apollo flight will provide for only a very short stay of two men on the surface of the moon, it would be premature to conjecture that there will exist a need for a great increase in the exploration capability immediately after the first landing. While there are groups studying the application of semi-permanent scientific bases on the moon's surface, a

practical assessment of the usefulness and the difficulty of
such projects can only be made after more information on the
moon is obtained. While some of this information may be
gathered by unmanned spacecraft, it would seem wise to await
the detailed evaluation that will be obtained from the knowledge brought back by the Apollo exploration teams.

The moon has been considered by some to be a useful military base. While it would be difficult to say that the moon
would have no use as a military base, it is quite obvious that
it is severely handicapped when compared to other installations that might serve the same purpose. It would cost 50
times as much to maintain a military base on the moon's surface as one of the same size in an earth orbit. Yet, the base in
earth orbit would in many respects be more effective and
would have no particular shortcoming in the comparison. Furthermore, it is very doubtful that even an orbital base would
have a worthwhile military potential in the near future.

Space flight to the moon will open for consideration the possibility of flight to nearby planets. Both Mars and Venus are
close enough to consider as possible targets for exploration in
the near future. Mars, however, has a much less hostile environment than Venus and will most probably be the next
world that man will set foot on after the moon. Venus is a
very interesting planet, however, and it is not unlikely that it
will prove useful to make close-up observations of Venus
when interplanetary flight is made possible.

The Radiation Environment of Space

Except for brief periods during launch and atmospheric reentry, the spacecraft operates in the environment of space.
Therefore, it is worthwile to devote some attention to the
environment of space prior to a detailed examination of the
spacecraft itself.

Although space is commonly thought of as being a vacuum,
there is a considerable amount of matter in space. The earth's
atmosphere persists to several hundred miles altitude, although 99.9 percent of the mass of the atmosphere is below a

level of 30 miles. The atmosphere is dense enough however, to cause sufficient drag on spacecraft in low orbits to cause them to slowly spiral into the earth.

Immediately beyond the earth's atmosphere, space is filled with charged particles that originate from the sun and become trapped by the earth's magnetic field. These particles form the Van Allen radiation belts. The particles in the belts are electrons and protons moving at high speeds. Since a magnetic field exerts a sideward force on a moving electrical charge, the path of the particles is continually being turned. Because the magnetic field exerts no force in the direction of motion, the velocity of the particles is not directly affected by the Earth's magnetism. Therefore, they continue to travel at a high velocity in close to circular paths. However, since each particle will most likely have some velocity, northward or southward, along the direction of a line of force in the magnetic field, it will tend to move along the line of force in a helical path instead of tracing the same circular path over and over again. The helical path will carry it toward either the north or the south magnetic pole of the Earth. Since the lines of force of the earth's magnetic field converge at the poles, they bunch up. The effect of this is that the north-south direction of motion of the charged particles are reversed in this region. Thus, the particles are trapped as they move in a high velocity helix north and south between the "mirror points."

The protons in the radiation belt have sufficient energy to be harmful to the crew of a spacecraft. It is important to avoid flying in the radiation belts for extended time periods, therefore, unless very heavy shielding is carried. The existence of the radiation belts makes it undesirable to make extended orbital flights at high altitudes. On the other hand, it is necessary to avoid the drag of the upper fringes of the Earth's atmosphere if the orbit is to last for an appreciable period of time. For a space station, an orbital altitude of approximately 250 miles appears to be a good compromise between the desire to avoid heavy shielding and the need for excessive propulsion to prevent the orbit from decaying.

While the radiation belts concentrate harmful protons

streaming from the sun, they also shield the region below the belts from these radiations. The sun not only radiates light and heat but it is also constantly throwing out protons and electrons. These particles are the constituents of hydrogen, which is the most plentiful element in the sun, particularly in the upper layers. Because of the great energy in the sun, the hydrogen remains ionized; that is, it remains broken down into electrons and protons, which are the ions of hydrogen. Normally, the flow of these ions does not have sufficient velocity to constitute a harmful radiation. This flow is sometimes called the *solar wind* and it is estimated to be at a velocity of 300 kilometers a second. It is estimated that there are from 100 million to 1 billion particles in each cubic meter of space at the earth's distance from the sun.

Occasionally, the sun will produce flares on its surface. During these flares, very high velocity particles are ejected. The protons resulting from these flares are harmful because of their very high velocity and it is necessary to protect the crew from excessive exposure. While it is known that the intensity of a solar flare may vary by several orders of magnitude, it is not possible to predict solar flare activity with confidence. Neither the time nor the size of the next flare occurrence can be reliably predicted. We do know that the appearance of a large group of sunspots indicates that a flare is likely. However, there is yet no way of deducing from this that a flare will be created, or for determining what its intensity will be if it does occur.

It is significant that sunspot activity is related to flare creation because sunspot activity is known to be cyclic. Since 1820, sunspot activity on the sun has been recorded by astronomers. They have determined that every 11 years sunspot activity is at a maximum. During the intermediate years, a minimum activity occurs. Thus, it can be said that during certain years the radiation hazard associated with space flight will be more severe than other years. The next period of extreme hazard will occur during 1967 and 1968.

In addition to the protons and electrons that are thrown out by the sun, there are other high-speed particles in space that should be mentioned. These are the cosmic rays. They travel many times faster than the particles from the sun. They have energies that may be as high as billion-billion electronic volts. That is about 100 thousand times as much energy as the most energetic solar protons may have. Cosmic rays are mostly protons. It is estimated that 84 percent of the cosmic rays are protons, while 14 percent are alpha particles, the nuclei of helium atoms. The remaining cosmic rays are the nuclei of heavier atoms, the majority being carbon, nitrogen, and oxygen. There are an insufficient number of cosmic rays to create a significant hazard to men in space.

The Thermal Environment of Space

The thermal environment of space must be considered from the standpoint that heat can only be transferred by thermal radiation in the space environment. This is unlike conditions within the earth's atmosphere, where heat may be transferred by both radiation and convection. In convective heat transfer, heat flows between the body and the fluid (liquid or gas) within which it is submerged, provided a difference in temperature exists between the body and fluid. Heat will always flow from the warmer to the cooler matter. Convective heat transfer occurs at the surface of the body where the molecules of the fluid come in contact with the surface. The greater the temperature difference the greater will be the heat transfer rate. The rate of heat transfer will also depend upon the rate of flow over the surface of the body. Thus a windy day will feel more chilly than a calm day, although the thermometer may read the same.

In the case of radiative heat transfer, heat is radiated in the same manner as light is transmitted. As a matter of fact, heat waves and light waves are quite similar. The human eye can detect radiated energy over a small range of wavelengths. Infrared radiations occur at wavelengths greater than the visible range. These are sometimes referred to as *heat radiations*. Energy, or heat, is transmitted by radiation regardless of the wavelength of the radiation. The rate at which a body may radiate heat from itself will depend upon the surface area, the condition of the surface, the temperature of the surface, and what the surface may be "looking at." If the surface faces the emptiness of space, it is essentially looking at nothing that is radiating significant heat and nothing that will reflect heat. In this case, heat will be radiated from the surface at a rate dependent only upon the temperature and the emissivity coefficient of the surface. The *emissivity* coefficient is merely a number that varies between 0 and 1 and describes how effective the surface is at radiating heat. A surface that is a perfect radiator would have an emissivity coefficient of one, whereas a surface incapable of radiating heat would have a coefficient of zero. Actually, most surfaces have coefficients that range from 0.1 to 0.9.

The effect of temperature is very important upon thermal radiation. The heat radiated to the black coldness of space is proportional to the fourth power of the absolute temperature of the radiating surface. This means that if the surface temperature were doubled, then heat would be radiated at 16 times as high a rate.

When light from the sun or any source strikes an object, some of the light energy will be absorbed. Some surfaces will absorb very little light and will appear to be white or very shiny, since most of the light striking the surface is reflected. Other surfaces will absorb essentially all of the light and will therefore appear to be black. The *absorbtivity* coefficient is the portion of the incident light absorbed by the surface. It should be noted that the absorbtivity and emissivity coefficients are equal to each other at any given wavelength. However, since these coefficients vary with wavelength, and since the energy being absorbed will most likely be at a different wavelength than the energy being radiated, the absorbtivity and emissivity will usually be different in the actual case. For instance, titanium oxide, which is an excellent pigment for white paint since it is so reflective, has a very high emissivity coefficient in the infrared spectrum. The consequence of this is that a surface painted with a titanium oxide paint will not only reflect away most of the sun's energy, but will also effectively radiate the heat that might be absorbed. Such a surface is said to have a high emissivity-to-absorbtivity ratio. It will have a low equilibrium temperature when bathed by the sun in space. There are surfaces that have low emissivity-to-absorbtivity ratios and they will have much higher equilibrium temperatures.

Figure 1-2 is a plot that shows the equilibrium temperatures that will exist for surfaces over a range of obtainable ratios of emissivity-to-absorbtivity when the surface is exposed perpendicular to the sun in space and a distance from the sun equal to that of the earth and Mars.

In the preceding discussion, it has been assumed that heat was not being transferred on the back side of the surface. In actuality, the spacecraft will quite likely always be dissipating heat by radiation, and the skin of the spacecraft will only rarely be perpendicular to the sun's rays. In fact, much of the spacecraft skin will not be facing the sun at all at any given time. The effect of non-perpendicularity is to reduce the heat input from the sun.

The temperature of the spacecraft will also be affected by the presence of other warm bodies, such as the earth or the

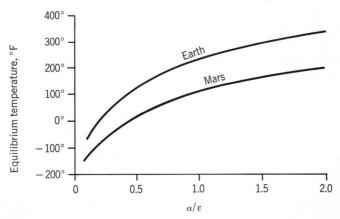

Fig. 1-2. Equilibrium temperature for an insulated surface facing the sun in space near Earth or Mars.

moon. Thermal radiation from the moon is particularly significant since its surface can get quite hot, and if the spacecraft
is close to the moon, it may receive a large heat flux from that
source. It should be noted that the energy coming from the
moon is in the same portion of the infrared spectrum that the
spacecraft may be attempting to dissipate heat by radiation.
(i.e., they are nearly at the same temperature as one another.)
The consequence of this is that the emissivity-to-absorbtivity
ratio must be nearly one. Therefore, it will not be possible in
the vicinity of the moon to achieve a favorable exchange of
heat for spacecraft surfaces facing the moon unless the spacecraft's surface is hotter than the moon's surface.

Meteor Environment

One of the most uncertain hazards of space flight is the danger of a damaging hit to the spacecraft by a meteoroid. There
is a great deal of evidence on the nature of meteoroids, but
the quantity of meteoroids of sufficient size to damage the
spacecraft can only be crudely estimated. Furthermore, meteoroids travel at velocities much greater than that which can
be suitably produced for small particles in the laboratory.
Thus, damaging effects can only be estimated and schemes for
protection against meteoroids cannot be tested under realistic,
controlled conditions.

Meteoroids are debris in the solar system that may come
from a number of sources. The majority of this debris is presumed to come from the disintegration of comets. Other likely
sources are from the fragmentation and ejecta from asteroids
as a result of collisions. Similarly, it is estimated that material
is ejected from the moon's surface when it is hit by other space
debris. It is considered likely that only a very small portion of
this debris is swept up from interstellar space as the sun
moves in its orbit in our galaxy.

When meteoroids of sufficient size happen to plunge into
the Earth's atmosphere, they leave a visible trail in the sky.
Such an atmospheric phenomena is called a *meteor* or a falling
star. If the meteoroid is large enough to reach the ground

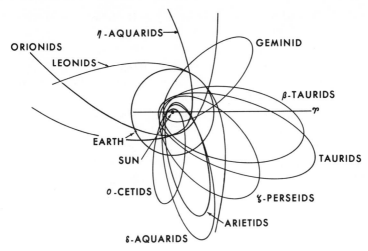

Fig. 1-3.   Orbits of meteor streams intersecting Earth's orbit. (NASA)

rather than being consumed in the atmosphere, such pieces that are found are called *meteorites*.

Observation of meteors has led us to conclude that some of the meteor activity is fairly predictable. At certain times of the year meteor showers occur. Furthermore, it has been noticed that certain of these showers are much more active during particular years. It is presumed that such showers are the manifestation of dead comets. Comets are known to have highly eccentric orbits. Such orbits may take them beyond the furthest planet at their aphelion, yet inside the Earth's orbit at perihelion. Now it is known that when a comet comes close to the sun it tends to disintegrate. It may be presumed that after sufficient time, the comet does indeed disintegrate and the debris from the comet eventually gets distributed around its orbit in a manner similar to Saturn's rings. When this happens, there is no longer any way of detecting the presence of the old comet, except for the occasional meteor showers that occur when the earth passes through the area of its orbit, which it may do every year. The intensity of the shower may vary from year to year. This is an indication that the material of the comet has not yet evenly distributed itself around its orbit.

In addition to the meteors that appear in showers, there is a great flux of sporadic meteors which appear in a random manner all year around. In fact, most of the meteors are not identified with the known showers.

The velocity of meteoroids has been measured by observing the passage of meteors. The vast majority of these have velocities greater than 11 kilometers per second, but less than 72 kilometers per second. The minimum observed velocity is the same as escape velocity from the earth. Particles with such velocities probably originated at the moon with just sufficient velocity to get free of the moon's gravity. The upper limit of velocity of 72 kilometers a second can be used to support the conclusion that most meteoroids originated within the solar system. The greatest velocity a particle can have when it is the earth's distance from the sun and yet remain in a solar orbit is 42 kilometers per second. If the earth's orbital velocity of 30 kilometers per second is added to this, then the observed maximum velocity of 72 kilometers per second is obtained.

Of great importance to the designers of the spacecraft is the size of particles that may be encountered as well as their velocity and density. We know that there are a great many more small meteoroids than large ones. Figure 1-4 is an estimation of the variation of weight with the number of particles which may be encountered by a square foot of surface during a day. This estimation is based upon sketchy data and may be off by as much as a factor of 10.

From the standpoint of the damage which can be inflicted upon a spacecraft, the density of the meteoroids is also significant. It is estimated that about 10 percent of the meteoroids are of asteroidal origin. The density for these may vary from 3 to 9 g/cm^3. The remaining 90 percent would be of cometary origin with a density that may vary from .05 to .5 g/cm^3.

Meteoroids hitting a spacecraft will impact with sufficiently high velocity to be vaporized. Their impact may be thought of as being similar to a small but very high intensity explosion. For this reason, the use of a meteoroid bumper or shield is

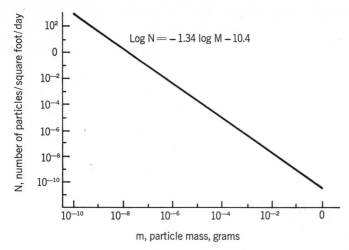

Fig. 1-4.   Average flux of meteors near the earth.

considered to be a practical scheme to afford protection against meteoroids of sufficient size to penetrate the main spacecraft structure. The bumper is a very thin sheet of metal fastened several inches outside of the frame of the spacecraft, covering vital structure and components of the spacecraft. When a meteor strikes the bumper, it is vaporized and its ability to damage the spacecraft is eliminated or greatly reduced. Although a bumper will not protect the spacecraft against all meteoroids, it should eliminate the hazard of all the smaller ones. There will always be the possibility that a meteoroid large enough to damage the spacecraft will be encountered. However, if the bumper is adequate, such a possibility will be sufficiently remote that meteoroid damage would no longer constitute one of the major hazards in the flight.

Environment of Other Worlds

The environment of the moon and the nearby planets must be an important consideration in any plans to put exploration teams on their surface. The environment of these worlds is extremely hostile, and elaborate measures must be taken to insure that both the spacecraft and their crew can safely operate on them.

The moon has a completely airless environment. The atmospheric density of the moon is estimated to be lower than that which can be produced in the finest vacuum equipment. The moon rotates at the same rate that it orbits the earth. Therefore, it shows only one face to the earth. This very slow rate of rotation produces nights and days that are each approximately two weeks long. During the day the surface temperature on the moon may rise to 240°F, whereas at night it may drop to −300°F.

Of greatest concern to the first astronauts to land on the moon will be some of the things that are as yet unknown about the moon. The surface can be seen to a fairly high resolution in the photographs taken by Ranger VII, VIII, and IX. But parts of the moon's surface could be extremely rough and yet look billiard-ball smooth in the photographs. Since there is no atmosphere, there can be no storms on the moon. Thus the only actions that form and shape the surface of the moon are volcanic action and meteoroids. The thoughts of the best scientists are in disagreement on what the surface may be like. It may be spongy rock froth, or a treacherous, loosely packed dust, or it may be rugged lava beds with crevasses and out-croppings of sharp rock. The surface features will be found to be a result of the environment that has existed on the moon's surface since its beginning.

The exploration of the moon will not only provide a great deal of knowledge in the strictly scientific sense, but will undoubtedly be the basis for deciding how rapidly we will undertake the exploration of some of the planets. Mars and Venus, being the closer planets, will be considered the major candidates for further adventures into space. While our knowledge of these planets is very limited, there are several facts that are known which will bear heavily on the problems of their exploration.

Venus is approximately the same size as the Earth with an

atmosphere which is probably poisonous and which may be at considerably higher pressure than that found on earth. The actual pressure, temperature, and composition of the atmosphere are of fundamental concern if men wish to land on Venus. The surface atmosphere of Venus, however, is still a mystery, since all we can see are the clouds of vapor which cover the planet. The rate of rotation of the planet cannot be clearly determined, and it is possible that Venus may have a very slow rotation. If this is the case, it would have a profound effect on the temperature and weather on the surface. With a very slow rate of rotation, there would be high surface winds, since the convective forces in the atmosphere created by the hot and cold sides would be very great.

Once the surface atmospheric conditions are determined, the problem of constructing a suit that could protect men on the surface might be very difficult. If indeed the atmosphere is poisonous (and it appears that it must contain high percentage of CO_2) then a major problem will be to prevent this atmosphere from leaking into the suit. This will be very difficult if the pressure outside the suit is greater than the pressure inside. It is likely that the exploration crew will be required to live in their suits at more than earth-normal pressure in the manner of underwater explorers. If the pressure is intolerably high, then the crew will not be able to leave their ship, but must do their exploration from within their vessel, as in the case of deep underwater exploration.

It is most probable that the temperature on the surface is much higher than on Earth. It is doubtful that it will be feasible to build a suit or even a spaceship that can function properly and sustain the lives of the crew in an atmosphere with a temperature very much greater than the temperature of the human body. Thus, if there are no locations on the surface of Venus with sufficiently low temperature, manned exploration may be ruled out for quite some time. There is a remote possibility that the polar regions of the planet may be cool enough to make exploration practical.

There is no real information on the nature of the surface of Venus. Different scientists have conjectured that it is an arid desert, is covered with water or other liquid, or is covered with dense tropical vegetation in a very wet climate. It is obvious that reconnaissance of the surface must be carried out before a landing can be made. Perhaps this could be best done by drones launched and controlled from a spaceship stationed in an orbit about Venus.

The exploration of Mars will undoubtedly be an easier task than exploring Venus. Because Mars has a very thin atmosphere, surface features can be easily seen and photographed from the Earth. Thus, there is much more known about Mars than Venus. Only the more important facts which are of interest from the standpoint of an expedition to Mars will be mentioned. The atmosphere of Mars probably contains some oxygen and water vapor. Therefore, large quantities of these essentials need not be carried to the surface, since a small amount of equipment should be able to extract them from the atmosphere. It may possibly be practical to replenish the stores aboard the space ship for the return journey to earth. The atmospheric pressure on Mars is far too low to sustain men without a pressure suit. Although the surface temperature is cold compared to the Earth, it is not an important consideration if the crew must be protected with pressure suits anyway. As a matter of fact thermal control within the suit will be greatly simplified if the design need only accommodate a cold environmnent. Disposing of the metabolic heat created within a space suit by the astronaut has always been a vexing problem that would be simplified by the thermal conditions expected on the surface of Mars.

There will be weather phenomena to contend with on Mars. Observers have reported seeing what appear to be clouds and dust storms. Also, there seems to be an early morning frost in the winter hemisphere that disappears during the day from the sun's heat. It will be important to find out considerably more about the Martian weather before a landing is attempted by man.

Mars rotates at about the same rate as the earth, taking only about 40 minutes longer to complete the day-night cycle. Thus, sunrise and sunset will take place on a familiar schedule, although the sun will, of course, appear much smaller.

Mars is predominantly red, and it is believed that the majority of the surface is like a desert. However, there are large, bluish-green patches on the surface which change in size and color with the seasons. These are most probably vegetation since they display many of the characteristics of vegetation on earth. Spectographic analysis of these areas are also in agreement with the vegetation hypothesis. The poles of Mars are covered with ice caps which grow and shrink with the seasons. During the period of ice-cap growth, the poles appear to be covered with clouds, which may indicate that the ice-caps are formed by snow fall rather than extra-heavy frost deposits. One of the most controversial features of Mars is the network of "canals" that a great many expert observers have been able to perceive when viewing with the eye. Nevertheless, there has been no photograph of Mars that has been of sufficient quality to confirm the presence of this feature. This is not surprising, since experience with astronomical telescopes has shown that the eye is better able to detect fine features than a photograph. The actual presence of the "canals" and their exact nature must await the attainment of better information on the planet.

A particularly interesting feature of Mars is the fact that it has two baby moons. These moons are extremely small and are in orbits that are very low compared to other natural satellites. Deimos, which is perhaps about eight miles in diameter, revolves in an orbit with a radius of 14,600 miles, whereas Phobus, about twice that size, is in an orbit only 5,800 miles in radius. These satellites will make excellent navigation aids to the astronauts as they approach Mars. They may be used as "landmarks" which will provide the navigator with a very accurate estimate of the distance and location of the center of gravity of Mars. They are so small that they have no significant gravity. Thus it will be very easy to "land" on them. It may even be necessary to provide some means of anchoring the spacecraft to the satellite to avoid the possibility of the vehicle drifting away. Their easy access may provide a means for setting up special instrumentation that could make continuous long duration observations of the planet. This information could either be stored for future exploration groups or transmitted back to the earth from time to time.

It may be a great many years before we will be able to travel to planets more distant than Mars and Venus. If we do, the next two candidates would be Mercury and Jupiter. Mercury is interesting, since its rotation is captured by the sun— one side always faces the sun, the other never sees the sun. The dark side of Mercury may be one of the coldest places in the solar system. This situation must have produced some very interesting effects on the geology of the planet. For instance, its atmospheric gases could have accumulated in layers on the back side as frozen deposits. Mercury may also be a valuable location to set up instruments for a solar observatory, since it would provide a protected location close to the sun.

Jupiter is so massive and hostile, it is doubtful that men will ever land on its surface. However, Jupiter's moons may some day receive human visitors. The larger of the moons may be the best candidate, since it is suspected that it may possess an atmosphere which would decrease the propulsive energy required to decelerate and land.

Trips to either Mars or Venus and back may last as long as a year or even more. The hazards of the space environment on these trips will be a vital consideration in designing the spacecraft and planning the mission. In the case of a trip to Venus, the intensity of solar proton radiation will increase as the distance to the sun is decreased. Similarly, it will become more difficult to keep the spacecraft adequately cooled. On the other hand, for a trip to Mars, the increased distance to the sun will reduce the energy received from the sun, which will discourage the use of solar energy for electric power. It is also believed that the meteoroid flux might be more intense at distances further from the sun than the earth's orbit.

2

Spacecraft and Crew

Characteristically, all spacecraft are as small and light as it is practical to construct them. Manned spacecraft are no exception. Mercury and Gemini are so small that they can only accommodate their occupants in the seated position. The great necessity to keep the spacecraft within the payload capacity of the launch vehicle affects the design of each piece of equipment. It is not only important that this equipment be light, but also that it be compact, because the entire spacecraft is made no larger than necessary.

A spacecraft is by far the fastest traveling vehicle in which a man has ridden. Yet its appearance may give no impression of speed. A spacecraft is designed for the environment in which it travels, and it is this consideration which leads to its shape and appearance. It must protect its occupants against the environment of space and therefore a compact shape approaching a sphere is the natural configuration for a spacecraft. This same shape most easily provides the structural strength to retain an atmosphere. It will also have the least amount of skin for a given volume. This is important in reducing the vulnerability to meteoroids, and in providing radiation shielding for the occupants. Reentry considerations also profoundly affect the shape. This subject is discussed in Chapter 8.

Mercury was America's first manned spacecraft. Apollo is our most highly developed spacecraft. There is a vast difference in the difficulty of the missions of these vehicles and consequently in their complexity. Although Apollo is in many ways similar in appearance to Mercury, a detailed comparison of these two spacecraft reveals a great many sophistications and improved capabilities incorporated into Apollo.

The Mercury spacecraft was launched into an orbit by the guidance system of its launch vehicle. The flight was then tracked by ground facilities. Other ground facilities computed its exact orbit and predicted its landing point. Therefore, the only active flight control function performed on board during a normal mission was the firing of the retrograde rockets. These were fired at a predetermined attitude at a time determined by computations carried out on the ground. In comparison to this, Apollo has complete capability to navigate and guide its flight through a series of complex maneuvers. Although it will also be assisted by ground facilities, it has sufficient equipment to do this in complete independence. In comparison to the Mercury retrorockets, Apollo carries three major liquid propulsion systems which may be started and stopped many times. Apollo's total propellant load is several hundred times as great as Mercury's.

The Apollo is designed to operate 250,000 miles away from home. Not only must a great quantity of information be communicated from this distance, but the time required for an emergency return may be as long as three days. This is in comparison to Mercury's emergency-return time of less than an hour.

Apollo also carries with it the Lunar Excursion Module (LEM) which is a completely independent spacecraft designed to land on the moon. This maneuver will be carried out in the unique environment of one-sixth earth's gravity in a vacuum on a surface that will never have been seen previously at close range by men. Later discussion will reveal how each of these considerations has led to unique development in design and operation.

The step from Mercury to Apollo may be compared to moving from the early Wright airplane to a transatlantic flight. It was such a great step that it was considered prudent to develop the Gemini spacecraft as an interim measure to increase our storehouse of knowledge experience with manned space flight, and specifically to learn more about space rendezvous and to learn more about longer periods of weightlessness.

The Gemini Spacecraft

The Gemini is a two-man spacecraft manufactured by the McDonnell Aircraft Company. Its most important mission is the investigation of the problem of rendezvous in space. This mission is carried out in conjunction with an Agena spacecraft that is previously launched into orbit by an Atlas launch vehicle. The Gemini is joined to the Agena in space and the remaining propellant in the Agena provides the Gemini astronauts with the opportunity to perform a number of maneuvers in orbit. These maneuvers, which are tracked from the ground, evaluate the precision of spacecraft guidance equipment. The Gemini is guided during reentry, for further evaluation of this equipment. The Gemini also provides the capability for the crew to remain in space for two weeks. Such extended stays in space are evaluated to assess extended space flight effects on the performance and health of the crew.

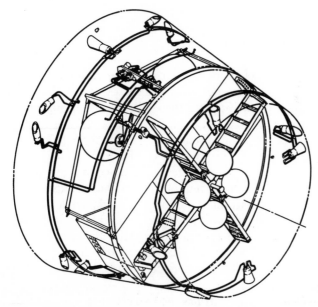

Fig. 2-1.   The Gemini adapter section. (NASA)

The Gemini is launched by a special version of the Titan II missile. The Titan has been modified for this purpose so that it is more reliable. The Gemini spacecraft is mounted on the second stage of the launch vehicle with a large conical adapter. The spacecraft and the adapter section weigh about three tons. They are separated from the launch vehicle at the time of insertion into orbit and remain united until the time for the retro maneuver at the end of the mission. The adapter is actually an important part of the spacecraft, since it contains the propulsion and power generation system for the spacecraft. The adapter is fitted with a great many small rocket engines, each individually controlled. The Gemini employs these rockets to carry out its mission maneuvers. They are arranged in a manner to facilitate both translational and rotational maneuvers. The rockets can be controlled either by the crew or by the Gemini guidance equipment.

The adapter also houses hydrogen-oxygen fuel cells and their supply of reactants which are stored at very low temperatures. A portion of the skin of the adapter is used as thermal radiators. These radiators cool the cabin, the fuel cells, and other heat-producing equipment such as electronic packages.

At the completion of the mission, the adapter is severed around its circumference by a shaped explosive charge. The rear portion of the adapter then falls away, leaving only the forward portion attached to the spacecraft. This uncovers the retrorockets for firing. From this moment throughout the remainder of the mission, the spacecraft's attitude may be controlled with an additional set of attitude-control jets mounted in the small cylinder in front of the astronauts. These jets may hold the spacecraft in the proper attitude while the retrorockets are fired, and are subsequently used to control the path taken during the reentry maneuver. After the retrorockets are fired, the remainder of the adapter is jettisoned with another explosive charge. The spacecraft is then left in its reentry configuration.

The Gemini spacecraft has the two astronauts seated side by side, but with the seats slightly canted away from each other.

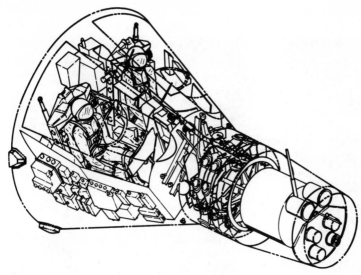

Fig. 2-2.   The Gemini reentry module. (NASA)

The astronauts ride in ejection seats and the outward canting
of the seats assures that they won't collide in the event of an
ejection. The position of the seats also makes best use of the
small space allowed for the cabin interior. The small end of
the Gemini spacecraft is its docking fixture. This end is in-
serted in a corresponding fixture on the forward end of the
Agena target vehicle. When properly driven together, the
docking fixtures latch together in much the same manner that
railroad cars couple.

The Apollo Spacecraft

The mission of the Apollo project is to land two astronauts
on the surface of the moon and then to return them safely to
earth. This mission is so complex that it will require the coordinated effort of a team of two separate spacecraft launched
together on the powerful Saturn V launch vehicle. Both the
command and service modules, which are made by North

Fig. 2-3.   The Apollo space vehicle. (NASA)

American Aviation, make up one partner of the team. The
lunar excursion module, which is made by Grumman Aircraft
and Engineering Corp. is the other partner. It is expected that
future exploratory missions to the planets will also use double
or even triple spacecraft to best perform the various phases
of the flight.

The command and service modules operate together as one

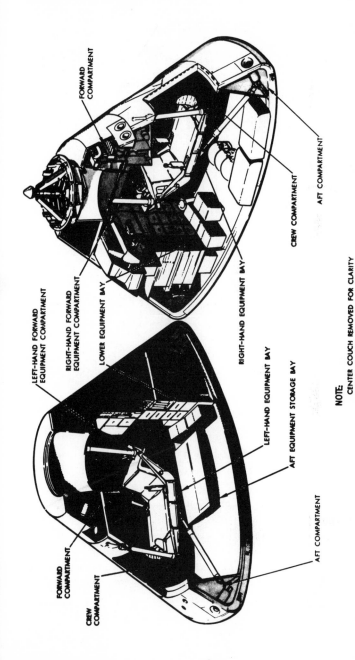

NOTE:
CENTER COUCH REMOVED FOR CLARITY

Fig. 2-4.   The Apollo command module. (NASA)

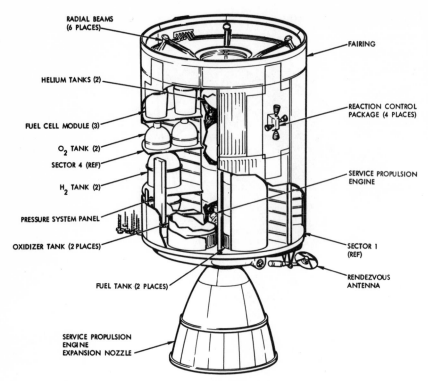

RADIAL BEAMS
(6 PLACES)

FAIRING

HELIUM TANKS (2)

REACTION CONTROL
PACKAGE (4 PLACES)

FUEL CELL MODULE (3)

O_2 TANK (2)

SECTOR 4 (REF)

H_2 TANK (2)

SERVICE PROPULSION
ENGINE

PRESSURE SYSTEM PANEL

OXIDIZER TANK (2 PLACES)

SECTOR 1
(REF)

RENDEZVOUS
ANTENNA

FUEL TANK (2 PLACES)

SERVICE PROPULSION
ENGINE
EXPANSION NOZZLE

Fig. 2-5.   The service module. (NASA)

spacecraft, and in this configuration are simply referred to as
the CSM. The command module is the portion that houses the
crew, whereas the service module, like the Gemini adapter,
provides power, propulsion, and cooling radiators. The lunar
excursion module, or LEM, is also a two-piece spacecraft.
There is a descent stage that provides the propulsive power
to descend from lunar orbit and land on the surface of the
moon. This stage also carries the lunar landing gear. The other
part is the ascent stage. This part houses the crew throughout
the LEM mission and has the propulsion system that launches
the LEM from the lunar surface into orbit, where it will
rejoin the CSM.

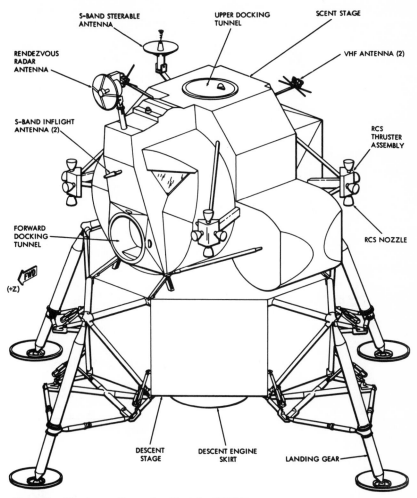

Fig. 2-6. The Lunar Excursion Module. (NASA)

The Apollo Mission Sequence

Before describing the features of the CSM and LEM in greater detail, it is necessary to discuss the manner in which they will be employed in carrying out the lunar landing mission. The mission will start with Apollo spacecraft assembled on top of the Saturn V. The command module will be on top of the stack, with its escape rocket in place. In this position, it and the astronauts are free to leave the rest of the assembly quickly if an emergency should occur during the launch. Directly beneath the command module and mated to it is the service module. If a launch abort does not occur, the command module will remain attached to the service module throughout the mission, until the time it is ready to reenter the atmosphere. The service module is supported on top the Saturn S-IVB stage by a long monocoque structure called the adaptor. The LEM is housed inside the adaptor and supported through its landing gear structure, which is folded and attached to the adaptor shell at four points. During launch the LEM remains unoccupied.

It is the job of the Saturn V to inject the Apollo spacecraft on a translunar flight path. The first two stages and part of the third stage will be used to achieve an orbit around the earth. The Apollo and the partially-used third stage will remain in this parking orbit for several hours. During this time, the Apollo crew will test and check various equipment to ascertain that they are indeed functioning in the space environment as intended. The parking orbit is desirable also from the standpoint that it permits the flight to be made during any day in the month rather than only when the moon is at a suitable position with respect to Cape Kennedy. At the proper position in the parking orbit, the third stage of the Saturn is started for the second time. This time it accelerates the Apollo spacecraft to the desired translunar injection velocity, shuts down, and is subsequently jettisoned.

After the third stage of the Saturn injects the Apollo spacecraft into its translunar trajectory, the LEM must become attached to the CSM to allow the service module propulsion system to maneuver this assembly into lunar orbit. Therefore, the Saturn third stage will be stabilized in a fixed attitude, while the CSM is separated from it. The astronaut crew will then rotate the attitude of CSM 180° so that the command module is facing the LEM, which remains attached to the

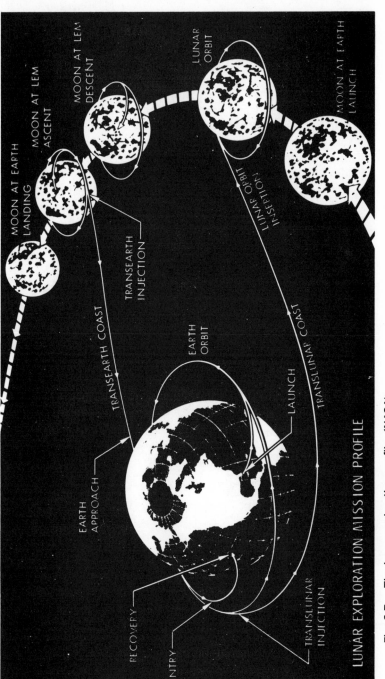

Fig. 2-7.   The lunar exploration profile. (NASA)

front of the Saturn third stage. Next, they will join the command module to the LEM by means of a docking attachment on the front of the command module. The docking maneuver will require a very precise control of the attitude and position of the command and service module, since contact must be made at very low velocity and with very little error in alignment. This maneuver has already been practiced many times on simulated spacecraft in training exercises. The astronauts also practice this maneuver in Gemini flights.

After the command module is joined to the LEM, its attachments to the Saturn are released and the LEM is pulled away. These various maneuvers are all made using the small reaction jets on the service module. The docking mechanism is arranged in the hatch of the command module and attaches

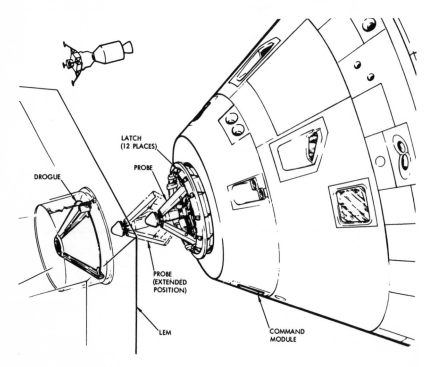

Fig. 2-8.   Apollo docking machinery. (NASA)

to the hatch of the LEM. When these modules are locked together, a pressure-tight seal is created. The hatch covers and the docking mechanism are then removed, allowing a pressurized passage between modules. Thus, the crew can occupy the lunar excursion module at will during the outbound portion of the mission, which will take about three days. However, the lunar excursion module does not have an active role during this mission phase.

The primary activity during the outbound journey is associated with navigation and guidance of the spacecraft. Based upon computations made aboard the spacecraft and on the earth, the Apollo spacecraft will probably make two or three mid-course corrective maneuvers during this period. These maneuvers are of small velocity and are used to correct the small errors the Saturn V guidance system made in inserting the Apollo into translunar flight. Such errors are so small that they can only be detected after a period of coasting.

The path that the Apollo will take to the moon is one that will cause it to pass within 100 miles of the back side of the moon. If it were allowed to coast past the moon, the lunar gravity would swing its path around and back to the earth. However, near the point of closest approach, the service module will be used to make a "de-boost" maneuver, which will retard its velocity just sufficiently to leave it in a circular orbit about the moon.

The Apollo will then remain in lunar orbit for a sufficient period of time for the astronauts to establish that the orbit is satisfactory. Then two of the astronauts will move into the LEM. The docking fixture will be replaced between the LEM and command module and the adjoining hatches will be shut. Then the LEM will be separated from the CSM.

While one astronaut remains in orbit with the CSM, the other two will descend to the surface of the moon in the LEM. The landing site will be near the lunar equator on the visible side of the moon. The LEM crew will be able to stay on the moon as long as a day while they carry out surface exploration in their immediate vicinity. During this period, they will set up several surface experiments which will continue to function and transmit data to earth after their departure. At the end of the lunar stay, the astronauts will launch the LEM ascent stage into an orbit that will intersect the orbit occupied by the CSM. The descent stage of the LEM will be left behind on the lunar surface. The LEM will then rendezvous and dock with the CSM while in orbit about the moon. The LEM crew will then transfer into the command module. The docking fixture will be left with the LEM, which will be abandoned in lunar orbit.

The service module propulsion will then be used to inject the CSM into the transearth path. This maneuver will have to be made on the far side of the moon. The return journey will take approximately three days and require several mid-course correction maneuvers. The service module will be jettisoned just prior to the time the command module reenters the earth's atmosphere. The command module will make a controlled deceleration in the atmosphere and be guided down to the near vicinity of one of several ships stationed in the Atlantic and Pacific oceans. The particular ship to which the command module will be guided will depend on such operational factors as the time spent during the mission and the local weather in the several recovery areas.

The Command and Service Modules

The command module is constructed to house the crew during launch and reentry and during translunar and transearth flight periods. During the launch period, it carries an escape rocket. The command module is built to be rugged enough to withstand launch emergencies and to reenter under very severe conditions which may result from an aborted mission. It is equipped with a guidance and navigation system, a stabilization and control system, reaction control jets, a communication system, a life support system and all the necessary accommodation for crew control of the spacecraft.

There are three crew stations. The crew are located in their couches in a side by side arrangement. There is a pilot, a navigator, and a flight engineer. The three astronauts must be in their couches during launch and reentry. During the remainder of the mission, only the left-hand station needs to be continually manned. The leg supports of the couches are constructed so that they can be folded out of the way when the couch is unoccupied. This creates additional space for the off-duty astronauts to move about. It also permits the navigator to move up to the navigation console, which is on the opposite side of the capsule from the flight panel. Since navigation is carried out only during the coasting portions of the flight, this location imposes no restriction on this activity.

The three couches are supported on shock-attenuating struts which allow the couches to move during a hard landing, thereby preventing the crew from being subjected to intolerable accelerations. The space under the couch that is left clear to accommodate this motion is used during the mission as a sleeping area. It can be isolated from the rest of the cabin by a curtain.

The service module is designed to support the command module. It contains the propulsion system used for most of the mission maneuvers, such as deboosting into lunar orbit and accelerating from the lunar orbit to the earth return trajectory. The service module propulsion will be employed for the guidance-correction maneuvers during both the outbound and return flight. The command module was designed to be as light as possible in order to reduce to a minimum the weight that reenters the atmosphere and is subsequently lowered on the parachutes. This produced weight savings in heat protection material and in the parachute system. Therefore, anything that did not need to be put in the command module was placed in the service module. Thus, the service module is equipped with a reaction control system, so that the command module's reaction control system need only be large enough to serve during reentry flight. Similarly, the command module carries only sufficient batteries and breathing oxygen to serve for that period of time starting with reentry when the service module is detached. The service module carries the main electrical power system, which is made up of three hydrogen-oxygen fuel cells. And the service module also carries the

high-gain directional antenna needed for reliable long-range
tracking and communications with earth stations.

The Lunar Excursion Module

The LEM and the command and service modules are quite
unlike. Since the LEM is protected during the launch by the
housing in which it is carried, it is never directly exposed to

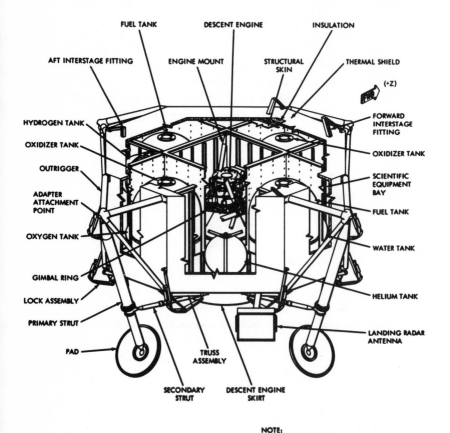

Fig. 2-9.   The LEM descent stage. (NASA)

the environment of atmospheric flight. It must, however, make a landing on an airless world and so the entire descent maneuver and subsequent landing will be carried out using the energy of rocket propulsion.

The descent maneuver will be similar to "backing-down" a launching trajectory. The landing maneuver will be somewhat similar to the landing of a helicopter. The descent stage will differ from most other rocket stages in that the engine will be throttleable and it will have a landing gear.

The cabin of the LEM is an integral part of the ascent stage. The ascent stage also carries all the active systems of the LEM. It is equipped with a guidance and navigation system, a stability and control system, reaction control jets, a life

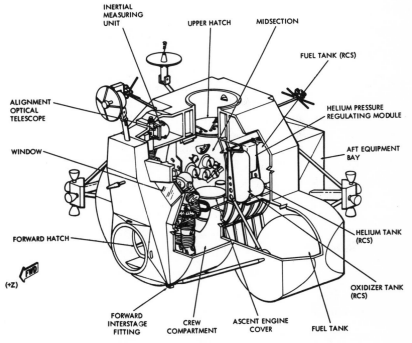

Fig. 2-10.   The LEM ascent stage. (NASA)

support system, a communication system, and an electrical power system.

The LEM design reflects several particularly important considerations associated with lunar landing. It has a very widespread landing gear and a low center of gravity. This is because, with the small lunar gravity field, the likelihood of overturning is greatly increased. The lunar weight of the vehicle is one-sixth of its earth weight. It will be the weight of the vehicle that produces the righting moment when only one or two of the landing pads are in contact with the lunar surface. The overturning moment (produced by the presence of some residual horizontal velocity at the time of initial contact) would remain the same on the moon as on earth. This is because the overturning moment is directly related to momentum, which, like mass, is independent of the local gravitational field.

The LEM's low center of gravity is achieved by locating the propellant tanks around the rocket motor of each stage. This is a departure from nearly all other rocket propulsion systems, wherein the propellant tanks are located above the rocket motor, since this arrangement is structurally more efficient.

The crew members are located in the most efficient manner for visibility from the LEM. They are supported in a standing position—much like the driver of a milk truck. The standing arrangement was chosen for several reasons. It saves weight. It allows the crew to easily move their heads to the window for external visibility, or back away from the window for optimum viewing of the flight control display, or to the sighting optics for navigational functions. Since the LEM is equipped with low thrust propulsion systems that produce barely one "g", the standing position is not expected to prove fatiguing during the periods the propulsion system is employed.

Spacecraft Propulsion

One of the most critical systems on a spacecraft is its propulsion system. If the propulsion fails, the spacecraft will be unable to return from a mission and the lives of the crew will be lost. In a manned spacecraft, the propulsion system should not only be immune from catastrophic failures, but it must start and operate reliably many times during the mission.

The propulsion systems on spacecraft are selected primarily on the basis of reliability as opposed to performance. Solid rocket motors are used whenever they are suitable, since a solid motor is simple and can be made extremely reliable. In the many applications for which solid rockets are unsuitable, liquid rockets using hypergolic, noncryogenic propellants are used. Hypergolic propellants will ignite upon contact and therefore the rocket engine need not be equipped with an ignition system. The avoidance of the use of cryogenic propellants, which must be kept in insulated containers, greatly simplifies the spacecraft's propellant storage and feed systems.

Only pressure-fed propulsion systems are currently being employed on manned spacecraft. In such systems, the force

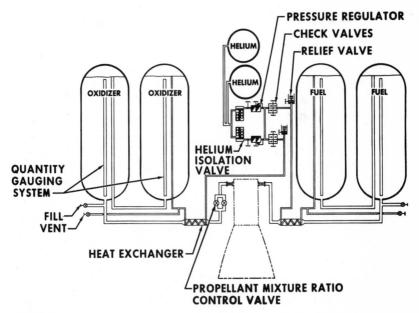

Fig. 2-11. A schematic diagram of the service module propulsion system. (NASA)

required to cause the propellants to flow into the rocket combustion chamber is created by pressurizing the propellant tanks with helium gas. Helium from high-pressure storage bottles is fed into the propellant tanks at the desired pressure through pressure regulation valves. Compared to conventional pump-fed propulsion systems, a pressure-fed system is considerably heavier since the propellant tanks must be made stronger and a great deal of helium pressurant must be carried in high-pressure containers. On the other hand, many simplifications are achieved. For instance, the number of valves and controls for start and shut-down are greatly reduced and the rocket motor's turbopump is eliminated.

Spacecraft are all equipped with small auxiliary rockets, used for attitude control and minor maneuvers. They may also carry large main propulsion systems for major maneuvers, as in the case of the LEM and CSM. Mercury and Gemini, however, used solid retro-rockets for their major maneuvers, and therefore needed no main propulsion.

It is common practice to carry an excess of auxiliary rockets arranged in a manner so that one or more of these rockets may fail without crippling the spacecraft. On the other hand, it is not practical to carry more than one main propulsion system. The designer must therefore design this system to be extremely reliable. One approach is to use redundant components wherever it appears to be practical. For instance, four valves arranged in a series-parallel arrangement may be used to replace a single valve. Such an arrangement protects the system against either a failure to open or a failure to close.

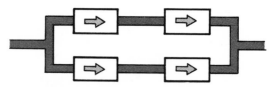

Fig. 2-12. This parallel-series arrangement of check-valves greatly increases reliability. If each valve had a reliability of .999, then the overall reliability for the arrangement would be close to .999997.

Spacecraft propulsion systems must be capable of starting in the weightless environment. It is therefore important that the propellant storage tank be arranged so that propellants rather than helium will always be transferred to the engine. The propellant tanks of the auxiliary propulsion system are manufactured with an internal bladder. The propellant is stored within the bladder and the helium pressurant is introduced outside of the bladder. Thus the bladder collapses as the propellant is expended and the bladder wall separates the helium from the propellant. The large tanks used in the main propulsion systems are not equipped with bladders. The auxiliary propulsion system must therefore be used for a short period to settle the propellant before the main propulsion may be started.

The Spacecraft Crew

A spacecraft is a very complex machine embodying the functions of a great many complex, highly developed systems. However, the most complex, highly developed systems aboard the spacecraft are the astronauts. The men aboard a spacecraft cannot match the specialized performance of the systems under their control. Their energies are feeble in comparison to the power generation and propulsion systems. They cannot match the inertial measuring system for sensitivity and response. They cannot compete with the computer for precision and speed. They cannot match any automatically operated equipment for untiring attention to monotonous tasks. The vital job that spacecraft crews perform is the management of all the various equipment and systems aboard the spacecraft, and in directing the mission operation. They are also able to inject the element of human intelligence in dealing with unforeseen situations. The characteristic ability of man to interpret a wide variety of unrelated information and data makes his presence highly desirable in any complex undertaking.

It is important that the spacecraft be designed to facilitate the display of information to the crew and their control over the spacecraft. The display panel should be laid out in a well organized manner, so that the crew can rapidly acquire and assess information related to all given operations or maneuvers. All the information to be monitored on a given system should be displayed in contiguous areas with appropriate switches nearby.

The most important displays are those associated with control of flight maneuvers, since these must be most easily coordinated with the control of the spacecraft. Such displays and windows used for the same purpose must be near each other and as near as possible to the center of the astronauts' vision envelope. It has been found advantageous to employ a side-by-side arrangement for locating the crew. This permits the use of common display equipment to present the same information to more than one man and facilitates an arrangement that allows one man to monitor the entire spacecraft while his companions are in an off-duty status.

In addition to monitoring and correcting the status of various equipment, the crew of a spacecraft communicates with the mission control center on earth in regard to mission and equipment status. During certain times, the crew may also become engaged in navigation and piloting. The crew's role in navigation is discussed in Chapter 4; some of the piloting tasks will be explained in the following.

Piloting tasks fall into two categories. First, there are those that can be done with optimum precision in a highly automated mode. In such cases the crew will usually monitor the maneuver in a stand-by status and take over control only in the event that a malfunction is indicated. The steering of the spacecraft during a major propulsion maneuver is an example of the above. While the spacecraft could be steered by the crew in accordance with computed instructions, an automatic steering mode will require less propellant as a result of greater precision. Thus, in cases such as these, the crew is best used to ascertain that equipment is functioning properly and to switch in other equipment, or take control in the event a malfunction occurs.

There are other piloting tasks that are of such a nature that they are best carried out under the direct control of the crew.

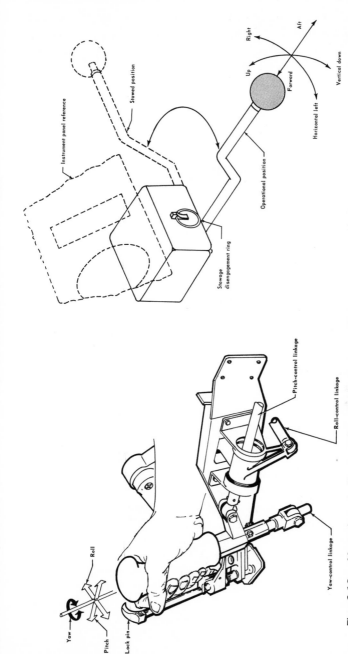

Fig. 2-13. Manual controllers: a three-axis hand controller is shown on the left and a translational maneuver controller is shown on the right. (NASA)

The docking maneuver has been proven to be one that is easily handled by an astronaut with fine precision and very little propellant consumption. On the other hand, it would take a great deal of additional complex, special-purpose equipment to automate this maneuver. In the docking maneuver, one spacecraft remains passive in a fixed attitude. The other spacecraft is controlled by an astronaut within it into the proper alignment, and then gently brought into contact with the passive spacecraft.

To carry out maneuvers of this type, the astronaut must control his spacecraft in both translation and attitude. He does this with a translation controller and an attitude controller. The translation controller will normally be held in the left hand, and the attitude controller in the right. The hand-controllers actuate electric circuits when they are moved. These circuits energize the propellant valves of the right combination of reaction control engines. For instance, if the astronaut wished to move to his left ($-Y$) he would move the translation controller left, and the reaction control engines labelled "4" and "8" in the LEM illustrated in Figure 2-14 would be fired.

For attitude control, it has been found that the astronaut's task is made much simpler and his control more precise, if a "rate command" system is used. With such a system, the motion of the hand controller sends signals to rate-sensing equipment which in turn controls the reaction control engines. The rate-sensing system will control the engines to produce a rate of rotation that is in proportion to the amount that the position of the hand controller has been deflected. With the controller in the neutral position, the rate command system would fire such engines as necessary to stop any residual motion, or to prevent disturbances from creating rotational motion. Thus the astronaut twists the hand controller sufficiently to rotate the spacecraft in the desired direction at the desired rate, and then returns the controller to center when the spacecraft has rotated to the desired position. This type of control is similar to the control exercised when steering an automobile. The rate of turning of a car is in proportion to the amount that

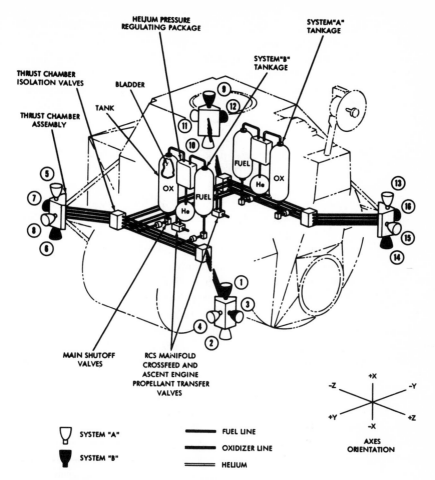

Fig. 2-14. LEM reaction control system. (NASA)

the steering wheel has been rotated, and a car stops turning when the wheel is centered.

The astronaut may also elect to control the spacecraft by the "acceleration command" mode. This would normally only be done in the event that the rate-sensing circuitry malfunctions. In this mode, the hand controller closes switches that directly energize the propellant valves of the reaction control engines. When the controller is deflected, the desired engines will fire and produce rotational acceleration.

The spacecraft will continue to rotate at an increasing rate until the controller is centered again. The engines then shut off and the spacecraft continues to rotate at the residual rate. To stop the rotation, the astronaut must deflect the controller in the opposite direction, which fires the engines that will retard the rotation. He must keep the controller deflected until that time when the motion is stopped and then bring the controller to the neutral position. While this is a relatively easy task when limited to one axis of rotation, it takes considerable skill to control the attitude about all three axes at one time.

The task is made particularly difficult since the reaction control engines cannot be expected to always produce balanced couples. The result is that cross-coupling is produced. In other words, the reaction control engines, when responding to a signal to produce rotation about one axis, may also produce some unrequested motion about the other two axes. To aggravate things further, translational maneuvers may also induce rotational motion since the thrust vector produced by firing a pair of engines for translation does not always go through the spacecraft's center of mass. Although it is considerably more difficult to control the spacecraft in the acceleration command mode, astronauts are able to develop sufficient skill to maneuver the spacecraft with precision in this mode. The acceleration command mode has the advantage of requiring a minimum amount of circuitry, thus it is less likely to malfunction. It therefore makes an excellent back-up to the "rate-command" mode which would ordinarily be used.

The landing of the LEM on the lunar surface will also require the direct participation by the crew. Although the guidance system aboard the LEM could steer the spacecraft down to contact with the lunar surface, this procedure does not account for the uncertainties in the landscape of the moon. Furthermore, the landing radar may not be as accurate as the crew in establishing the final rate of descent. On the other hand, it will require the precision and sensitivity of the guidance equipment to steer the LEM from orbit to a hover at a low altitude above the lunar surface. Therefore, the guidance equipment will do the steering until the crew feel that adequate visual contact has been made with the small detail features of the surface. From this point on, they will control the motion of the spacecraft, keeping the guidance system in a stand-by status for automatic hover if required.

The LEM will be maneuvered in somewhat the same manner as a helicopter. The thrust of the descent engine will be modulated to maintain altitude or to set the rate of descent as desired. The LEM will be made to move over the surface of the moon by tilting it so that the thrust of the descent engine has a horizontal component in the desired direction. The same thing will be done to halt undesired horizontal motion. The LEM will have sufficient propellant to hover over the lunar surface in this manner for approximately two minutes. During this period, the astronauts must fly to a visually selected

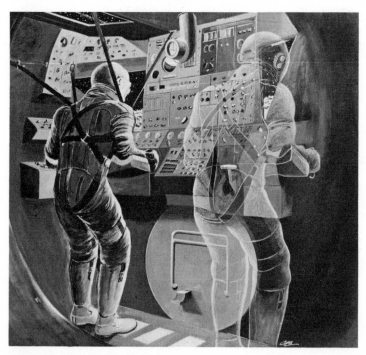

Fig. 2-15.   The LEM crew station. (NASA)

location and descend to a landing. Otherwise they will have to abort the landing and return to orbit with the ascent stage.

One of the difficulties the astronauts may expect to encounter during the landing will be associated with visual determination of altitude. This will be caused by the fact that there will be no familiar objects on the moon from which a reference distance can be established. A crater 50 feet in diameter at 100 feet altitude will give the exact same impression of distance as one 50 yards in diameter at 100 yards altitude. To help alleviate this situation, the astronaut will be able to refer from time to time to an altitude indicator driven by the guidance equipment and the landing radar. It is also intended to land in a location where the sun will be behind them at an elevation angle between 20° and 50°. This will not only provide adequate visibility of surface features, but will permit the astronauts to see the shadow of the LEM. Knowing the size of LEM's shadow and that they must land on it, will enable the crew to judge their altitude, rate of descent, and moment of contact with great precision.

3

Launching the Spacecraft

The launching of a spacecraft is one of the most important and difficult phases of the mission. The combination of a spacecraft and its launch vehicle is called a space vehicle, and it is therefore the space vehicle that must successfully carry out the launch maneuver. The launch vehicle is the active element in that it not only provides the energy for the launch, but it is also equipped with a guidance and control system which stabilizes and directs the motion of the space vehicle during the launching maneuver. However, the spacecraft can profoundly affect the operation of the launch vehicle by the aerodynamic forces it might produce, and more subtly by its effect on the structural dynamics of the space vehicle.

The large number of failures of missiles and space vehicles during launch attest to the fact that the launch phase is an extremely hazardous period. For this reason, the spacecraft is not completely passive during launch. It is equipped to detect failures aboard the launch vehicle and to implement a suitable means of escape for the crew.

Aerodynamics

Aerodynamic forces during the launch flight are of great concern and have been the cause of, or a contributor to many launch failures. Furthermore, aerodynamic forces are the primary contributor to the violence of a failure, regardless of what the cause may have been.

The governing parameters in the study of the aerodynamic environment of flight are *dynamic pressure* (q) and *Mach number* (M). Mach number is the ratio of air speed to the local velocity of sound. The following simple equation may be used to determine Mach number.

$$M = \frac{V}{a}$$

where M = Mach number, V = velocity of flight in ft/sec, and a = velocity of sound in ft/sec.

The dynamic pressure is a parameter that is used by engineers to conveniently express aerodynamic forces, loads, and moments. The dynamic pressure may be determined by this equation:

$$q = \frac{p \cdot V^2}{2}$$

where q = dynamic pressure in lbs/sq. ft, p = density in slugs/cubic ft, and V = velocity in ft/sec.

The dynamic pressure is thus proportional to the density and the square of the velocity. The various loads acting on the launch vehicle are the product of the dynamic pressure, the pressure coefficient, and the area involved. Thus it can be seen that the higher the dynamic pressure, the greater will be the various loads.

During a launch, the space vehicle travels upward while

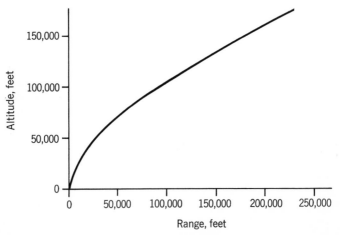

Fig. 3-1.   Flight path of a typical launch vehicle.

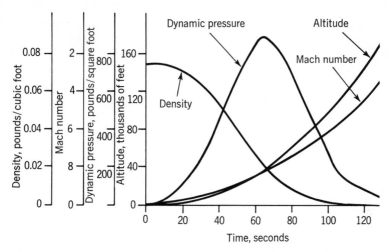

Fig. 3-2. The time history of altitude, density, Mach number, and dynamic pressure experienced during a typical flight of a launch vehicle.

accelerating. The air density is decreasing and the velocity is increasing during this time. The flight path during a typical launch is shown in Figure 3-1, and the time history of the altitude, dynamic pressure, and Mach number during this period are shown in Figure 3-2. It can be seen that the dynamic pressure first rises, then reaches a maximum value, then decreases during the flight. This is because immediately after launch, altitude is being gained slowly and the decrease in density is far less significant than the increase in velocity. Later in the flight, altitude is being gained so rapidly that the resulting decrease in air density more than compensates for the rate at which velocity is being increased. It is also important to note that the dynamic pressure is very large in the transonic region.

Aerodynamic Noise

There are several aerodynamic effects which may be significant during the launch. These are aerodynamic noise, stability, and drag. *Aerodynamic noise* is a manifestation of local unsteadiness in the flow of air over the space vehicle. Sharp turns and bumps in the external contours are a major cause in creating violent disturbances in the air flow. On the Mercury space vehicle, for instance, the external flow was greatly disturbed by the ridge created where the capsule was clamped to the booster. Immediately downstream of this location, the flow of air continually separated and reattached itself to the external surface of the vehicle in a violent and random manner. The consequent rapid changes in pressure created a noise which rose to a maximum level of about 165 decibels. This is about the same intensity as the noise created by the rocket engines. Noise of such intensity may not only be harmful to the crew, but can also destroy or weaken the structure of the space vehicles if it is not properly stiffened to resist the fluctuating loads generated. It is considered most probable that the structural failure of the first Mercury-Atlas space vehicle was caused by aerodynamic noise.

The crew member is protected from aerodynamic noise by the attenuation achieved in the capsule structure and the helmet of his space suit, which is fitted with padding in a manner to provide maximum protection to his ears. These protective measures were sufficient to allow the crew to maintain radio communication with ground personnel throughout the Mercury and Gemini launch periods.

Stabilization and Control

The great majority of space vehicles are aerodynamically unstable. In an unstable vehicle, the aerodynamic forces acting upon it tend to oppose its attitude of flight from the intended one of nose forward. If acted upon only by aerodynamic forces, the space vehicle would soon tumble. Therefore, it is necessary that stability be artificially provided. This is usually done by continually changing the direction of thrust by swivelling the rocket engines.

In considering the effects of aerodynamic forces on stability, it might be best to discuss the relationship of center of pres-

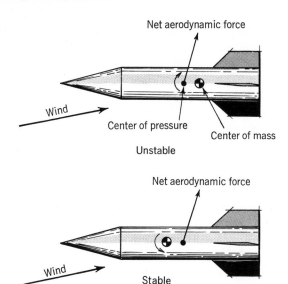

Fig. 3-3. Stability is achieved by placing the center of mass ahead of the center of pressure.

sure and center of mass of the space vehicle. This is illustrated in Figure 3-3. The *center of pressure* is the point where the combined effect of all aerodynamic side forces can be considered as concentrated. Such aerodynamic side forces are produced when the space vehicle is not flying straight into the wind but at some angle-of-attack to the wind. If the center of pressure is either ahead of or behind the center of mass, then a movement tending to rotate the vehicle will be produced. If the center of mass is behind the center of pressure, this will tend to rotate the space vehicle to a greater angle-of-attack. Since the side force will increase as the angle-of-attack increases, it is obvious that a counteracting movement must be produced or the vehicle will tumble. On the other hand, if the center of mass is ahead of the center of pressure, then the vehicle is said to have weather-cock stability in that it will naturally tend to point its nose in the direction it is travelling through the air.

It was already mentioned that most space vehicles are aero-dynamically unstable—the center of mass is behind the center of pressure. This condition could be corrected aerodynamically by attaching large fins to the after portion of the launch vehicle, but it is usually undesirable to do this because fins tend to lose their effectiveness at high Mach numbers, and would thus have to be very large to work satisfactorily at these speeds. Large fins would not only be very heavy but would also provide an excess of stability at low speeds, which would make steering the vehicle unnecessarily difficult.

The common method used to provide stability is to mount the rocket engines on gimbals so that the direction of their thrust may be turned by swivelling the rocket engine. It is necessary to continually swivel the engines during flight since the upsetting forces continually change with changes in angle-of-attack. The control system which swivels the engines is always seeking to balance the upsetting aerodynamic moments with restoring moments produced by the thrust of the engines. This is somewhat like the exercise of balancing a long stick vertically on your finger tip by continually moving your finger under the stick to keep it upright. The control system must respond very rapidly when the space vehicle is flying at high dynamic pressure, since at this time it becomes quite sensitive to small changes in angle-of-attack. A sluggish control system would allow the upsetting forces to build up faster than the restoring forces being applied by the engine. An adequate control system must therefore move the rocket engines rapidly back and forth, checking and correcting all disturbances.

The problem of steering is greatly complicated by the fact that space vehicles are usually very flexible. A typical propulsion stage of a launch vehicle is constructed to carry as much propellant as possible. Consequently, the structure is very light. The combination of a light structure supporting a large mass of propellant results in a great tendency for the assembly of stages and spacecraft to whip and bend when control forces are applied by the swivelling engines. It is necessary to design the control system so that it does not move so rapidly as to excite the flexible structure and thereby cause it to oscillate violently at one of its natural frequencies. At the same time, it is important to mount the attitude-sensing elements of the autopilot which steers the engines in a location that will be least disturbed by the bending of the structure. Otherwise, the autopilot could mistake the flexing of the structure for real deviations in space vehicle attitude and generate confused and erroneous steering signals.

Crew Escape from Launch Failures

There are schemes by which the crew may be carried away from the launch vehicles when a failure occurs or is about to occur. The entire capsule in which the crew is riding may be carried away by an escape rocket or the crew may be ejected from the space vehicle in individual ejection seats. When an escape rocket is employed, it must provide sufficient thrust to rapidly accelerate the capsule away from the launch vehicle, while at the same time overcoming the aerodynamic drag. In the Mercury flights, an escape rocket which produced 50,000 pounds of thrust for a period of about a second and a half was used. Apollo will be equipped with a rocket which has 150,000 pounds of thrust and an action time of about four seconds. In both of these applications, the escape rocket is powerful enough to rapidly accelerate the spacecraft away from its launch vehicle, even though the escape maneuver is initiated when the dynamic pressure is nearly maximum and the space-craft drag quite high. These escape rockets are also able to lift their spacecraft from the launch pad to several thousand feet, providing sufficient altitude for parachute deployment.

The Gemini astronauts ride in ejection seats. Ejection seats are not able to provide as rapid an escape from the vicinity of the launch vehicle as an escape rocket. However, the launch vehicle employed in the Gemini program uses propellants which will not explode with the same violence as the propellants used in Mercury and Apollo. This launch vehicle, which is a modification of the Titan II missile, uses hypergolic propellants. The fuel and oxidizer components of ordinary propellants might become intimately mixed with each other before some external source ignites them. When they then explode, the entire mass that is mixed goes off at once. In the case of hypergolic propellants, the reaction between the oxidizer and fuel is instantaneous upon contact. The very small amount that reacts in the immediate vicinity of contact blows the remaining portions away from each other. This action thereby limits the energy released to that resulting from the localized reaction.

Although the ejection seat is adequate to carry the crew clear of the Gemini launch vehicle, its operation is not without a certain amount of hazard. When the crew is ejected from the capsule at high dynamic pressure, they are exposed to wind blast and large drag forces. The ejection seat must be so designed that the arms and legs of the occupant are not allowed to flail in the wind; otherwise, they could easily be broken. At the same time, the seat should not tumble too rapidly, since the occupant would then be experiencing rapid changes in the direction of the drag forces encountered. This motion may greatly aggravate the effects of deceleration by moving his organs about within his body, and if he is not tightly confined to the seat he may be battered by the seat itself. For this reason, extensive tests were carried out under simulated conditions, with dummies, to ascertain that the motions and the forces to which the crew may be exposed do not exceed a safe level.

Escape rockets and ejection seats are needed only during the early portion of the launch, when the space vehicle is still within the atmosphere. There is no necessity for the crew to make an escape from a launch vehicle failure if it occurs outside the atmosphere, because such failures cannot produce hazardous conditions. Outside the atmosphere, there are no aerodynamic forces to cause the space vehicle to break up if it goes out of control. This eliminates one of the major hazards. The other hazard—explosion—is also of negligible concern outside the atmosphere. This is because there is no suitable mechanism in the absence of an atmosphere to bring large quantities of fuel and oxidizer into contact with each other. While a small explosion may occur in the engine area where fuel and oxidizer are being brought together, the force of an explosion does not carry well in a vacuum, and it is estimated that the capsule structure would not be damaged. Thus the procedure in the event of a falure in space would be to terminate the thrust of the launch vehicle, and then separate the capsule from the launch vehicle in preparation for reentering the atmosphere. If the launch vehicle were to fail at velocities greater than orbital, such as may be the case in an Apollo mission, then the spacecraft propulsion system may be used subsequent to separation from the launch vehicle to assist in redirecting the flight of the spacecraft to a return maneuver that will accommodate landing at a desired location.

Propulsion Considerations

Launch vehicles are usually made up of several stages. This is the only practical way that large payloads can be accelerated to space flight velocities. Rocket thrust is obtained from the reaction force that is produced when the propellants are accelerated in the rocket engine and expelled at a high velocity. The higher the velocity at which the propellants are expelled, the greater will be the thrust for a given rate at which the propellants are being consumed. The basis upon which rocket engines are rated is the thrust produced divided by the rate at which propellants are expended. This rating parameter is called specific impulse and it is defined by the equation:

$$I = F/M$$

where I = specific impulse in seconds,* F = thrust in lbs, and M = propellant flow rate in lbs/sec.

Rocket engines that use the chemical reaction of the propellants as a source of energy may produce specific impulses as high as 450 seconds. However, 300 seconds is a more typical

---

* It is recognized that the dimension, seconds, used for specific impulse annoys those sophisticates who object to dividing force by weight; however, it has come to be accepted by common use.

value. It is possible that, sometime in the future, nuclear-powered rockets can be developed with much higher performance. Since the main use for rockets is to accelerate a payload to very high velocity, the relationship between specific impulse and the velocity that can be achieved by a stage will be explained. It should be pointed out that some of the thrust of a rocket is usually dissipated in overcoming drag and gravity. These effects will be overlooked in this explanation in order to concentrate on the more important considerations.

As propellant is expended, the weight of the space vehicle becomes less. This means that the rocket engine is pushing against a mass that is progressively being reduced. Consequently, the acceleration is lowest at the time a stage is ignited and highest at the time of burnout. Thus the expenditure of a given quantity of propellant is much more effective in accelerating the space vehicle near stage burnout, than the same quantity would be when the stage is nearly full of fuel and quite heavy. As a matter of fact, equal amounts of velocity will be gained when equal percentages of the total weight are burned. Thus the velocity obtained from a stage is related to the ratio of the stage's initial weight to its burned-out weight.

The velocity that may be gained by a stage is shown in

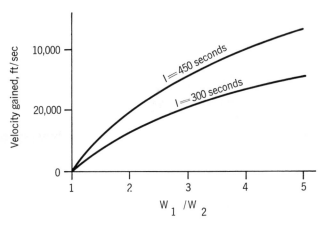

Fig. 3-4.   Velocity that may be gained by a propulsion stage.

Figure 3-4. This Figure shows the effect of specific impulse and the weight ratio of the stage. In order to get high velocities, very large weight ratios may be required. For instance, the initial weight must be about 4.8 times the burned-out weight to achieve 15,000 ft/sec., with a specific impulse of 300 seconds. Thus, there would be 3.8 pounds propellant for every pound of inert weight. A great deal of the inert weight is needed for engines, control system, tanks, and structure, leaving perhaps only 15 percent of the initial weight for payload. If higher velocities are desired, the payload must be smaller. However, even if the payload were reduced to nothing, the stage would still be able to achieve only a slightly larger velocity, since the inert weight of the stage would limit the weight ratio of the stage to perhaps ten to one. For this reason, when high velocities are desired, it becomes necessary to use more than one stage.

The advantage of staging is shown in Figure 3-5. Here it is assumed that a launch vehicle may be made of one, two, or three stages. Each stage is assumed to be constructed so that 10 percent of its weight is used for structure, engines, controls, propellant tanks, and other non-consumable parts. The remaining 90 percent is the propellant that is burned by the stage. It is further assumed that each stage contributes an

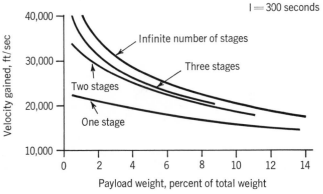

Fig. 3-5. The performance of multi-stage propulsion systems.

equal share to the total velocity gained by the launch vehicle. The advantage of using multi-stage launch vehicles is seen to lie in those applications where a high velocity is desired. The launch vehicle with an infinite number of stages is of course just a theoretical case, but is included to illustrate how a certain number of stages can achieve close to ideal performance at various velocities. Unless significant performance gains can be made, a minimum number of stages should be used, since each stage represents additional cost and an additional chance for hardware to malfunction.

Saturn V Launch Vehicle

The Saturn V, which will launch the Apollo lunar landing missions, is the free world's largest launch vehicle. It is shown in Figure 3-6. With the Apollo payload, it weights over 3,000 tons at lift-off, and would tower over a 30-story building. The Saturn V is a three-stage vehicle whose third stage is capable of being restarted. This restart feature permits the third stage to depart from a parking orbit after partially depleting its propellants in achieving the orbit.

The first stage of the Saturn V is designated the S-IC. It is constructed by the Boeing Company. It is 138 feet long and 33 feet in diameter. The propellants are liquid oxygen and RP-1, which is a petroleum product. This stage carries almost 4,500,000 pounds of propellant, which is consumed in two and one-half minutes. The dry weight of the stage is slightly less than one-fifteenth of the weight of the propellant it carries. The S-IC is powered by five F-1 rocket engines. Each of these engines produces one and one-half million pounds of thrust at sea level. The engines are arranged with the outer four mounted on gimbals and the inner engine fixed. The stage has four small fins, which are insufficient for aerodynamic stability, but are carried to reduce the difficulty of controlling the flight attitude. These fins are mounted on wind-deflecting fairings that minimize the aerodynamic load on the engines. This greatly alleviates the burden on the control actuators which swivel the engines on their gimbals.

Fig. 3-6.   The Saturn V with Apollo payload. (NASA)

The S-II is the second stage of the Saturn V. It is constructed by the North American Aviation, Inc. It is the same diameter as the first stage, but shorter. This stage burns liquid oxygen and liquid hydrogen propellants. This propellant combination produces about one-third more specific impulse than the propellants used in the first stage. This improvement in performance is partially cancelled by the problems associated with lower density of liquid hydrogen and the very cold temperature of −423°F. at which it must be carried. The S-II employs five J-2 rocket engines arranged in a manner similar to the engines on the S-IC stage. Each of these produce 200,000 pounds of thrust. This stage carries about 930,000 pounds of propellant. The dry weight of the S-II is slightly less than one-thirteenth the weight of the propellants it carries.

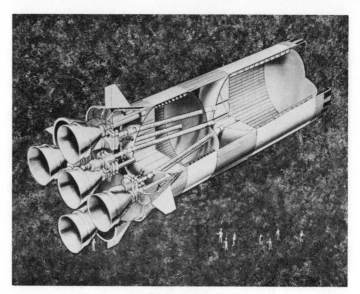

Fig. 3-7.   The Saturn S-1C stage. (NASA)

Fig. 3-8.   The F-1 engine. Five of these power the S-1C. (NASA)

This compares unfavorably with the dry weight ratio of the first stage and is a result of the low density of the hydrogen fuel which requires a very large tank.

The S-IVB is the third stage of the Saturn V. It is constructed by the Douglas Aircraft Company. It is powered by a single J-2 rocket engine and, like the S-II stage, its propellants are liquid hydrogen and liquid oxygen. The tanks of the S-IVB are 18 feet in diameter and contain about 230,000 pounds of propellant. The dry weight of this stage is about one-eleventh of the weight of the propellant it carries. This dry weight, which is relatively heavy in comparison with the S-II, may be explained by the fact that the S-IVB must be capable of being partially used in attaining a parking orbit, remaining in orbit for up to a day, and then being used a second time to accelerate the Apollo spacecraft to translunar velocity. The hydrogen tank must carry insulation to avoid excessive boil-off of propellants during the period in the parking orbit.

The S-IVB also carries ten small auxiliary rocket motors that burn hypergolic propellants. They are carried with their propellant tanks in two externally mounted pods. These motors are used for roll control during powered flight, and for three-axis attitude control at other times. They are also used to settle the liquid oxygen and liquid hydrogen propellants prior to the restart of the J-2 engine.

The brains of the Saturn V is called the instrument unit. It is mounted in a short cylindrical section on top of the S-IVB stage. This unit houses the guidance and control components and the vehicle's electronic intelligence system. The tracking equipment and associated electronic networks are also carried here.

4

Navigation, Guidance, and Control

One of the most challenging tasks facing the engineers developing the Apollo spacecraft is the creation of a navigation and guidance system which will operate with sufficient precision and reliability to permit our astronauts to travel to a remote destination on the moon and return safely.

Navigation in space requires the determination of position and velocity relative to the desired path or destination, and relative to the centers of significant gravitational masses. Also required is the computation of future positions and thereby the prediction of error by which a desired future position will be missed. Finally, the proper corrective maneuver must be determined. These tasks in navigation can be done aboard the spacecraft or by mission control facilities on earth.

Guidance consists of formulating and transmitting instructions to a control system that steers the spacecraft through a maneuver. A maneuver in space is done by propulsively accelerating the spacecraft by the correct amount and in the proper direction. By this means, a velocity vector is added to the spacecraft's initial velocity that places the spacecraft on the desired flight path. This is called a translation maneuver. Rotational or attitude control maneuvers must also be carried out by the control system. Such maneuvers may be needed prior to the translational maneuver to produce a desired heading prior to accelerating the spacecraft. Attitude control is also used to facilitate the aiming of antennas and to provide the crew with visual observations as needed.

Equipment

The tasks described cannot be performed by the crew without assistance. A great deal of equipment is carried to assist the crew. The equipment carried on the Apollo spacecraft is a good example. There is a space sextant and a sighting telescope which are optical instruments used to make angular measurements of the position of earth, moon, and sun relative to the star field, which is used as a fixed inertial reference. The optical instruments are rigidly mounted to the base of an inertial measuring unit so that the optical measurements may be compared for position determination. Optical measurements are also used to align the inertial measuring unit and to correct subsequent misalignments which may occur. The inertial measuring unit is a stabilized platform upon which are mounted integrating accelerometers. In addition to maintaining an angular inertial reference, the inertial measuring unit senses velocity changes in any direction.

The Apollo carries a rather sophisticated digital computer which acts on data from the optical equipment and the inertial measuring unit to solve both the navigation and the guidance problems.

Apollo is also equipped with an autopilot. The autopilot is used primarily to maintain control of the attitude of the spacecraft. It has inertial sensors and logic circuits, by which it is able to determine attitude errors. (The inertial measuring unit consumes a great deal of power and is used sparingly.) Attitude errors are corrected by attitude-control jets, which are controlled by the autopilot. The autopilot is also able to perform guidance maneuvers with marginal precision, in the event that the guidance and navigation computer, or the inertial measuring unit, have failed.

The actual energy used to make velocity or attitude maneuvers must, of course, be produced by rocket propulsion. Spacecraft such as Apollo are equipped with main propulsion systems that can be used to make large changes in velocity. There are also a great number of small auxiliary rockets, arranged in such a manner that they can effect either rotational maneuvers or minor translational maneuvers. It is common practice to carry an excess number of the small auxiliary rockets so that the failure of several of these will then not cripple the spacecraft.

Orbital Flight

All motion in space, including that of a spacecraft, is governed by the laws of orbital mechanics. There is no place within the solar system where a body can move without being subject to these laws. When in the vicinity of the earth, the earth's gravitational field will rule and the motion is then termed an earth orbit. However, the earth and the objects in orbit about it are all in orbit about the sun. Since the sun is so far away, its influence on these bodies is essentially identical and the motion of bodies orbiting about the earth appears to ignore the influence of the sun. Actually, the orbital velocity of earth about the sun is far greater than the relative velocity between earth and its satellites. Figure 4-1 illustrates the motion of the earth and a satellite relative to the sun.

The discussion of a few space missions will illustrate the concept that orbital motion is always used in space travel. The first example concerns the problem of transportation to a space station in earth orbit. The ferry vehicle would first ascend into an earth orbit. Once in orbit, the crew of the ferry vehicle would compare their orbit with that of the space station and then maneuver into a transfer orbit that would bring them to the station. Upon arrival at the station, they would maneuver once more to match the space station's orbit. The problem of traveling to the moon is identical to the above, since the moon is in orbit about the earth just as the hypothetical space station. The only difference is that once the spacecraft approaches the vicinity of the moon, the moon's gravitational influence on the spacecraft's motion increases. When the spacecraft gets near enough, the moon's gravitational field predominates and the spacecraft motion is that of an orbit about the moon and the earth's gravitational field becomes only a perturbing factor.

Fig. 4-1.   Paths of the earth and an earth satellite relative to the sun.

Flying from the earth to another planet, such as Mars, is quite similar, only in this case an orbit about the sun would be used. The navigation scheme would be to select an orbital path which intersects the orbits of Earth and Mars at those times when position of these planets are at the points of intersection. Thus, traveling to Mars will be done by traveling along the proper orbit about the sun. During the departure period, the earth's gravitational field will profoundly influence the motion, and similarly, at the time of arrival, the gravitational attraction of Mars must be dealt with.

Orbital Mechanics

A few simple concepts about orbital mechanics will be discussed in this section to provide the reader with a "feel" for space flight.

The simplest orbit is a circular orbit. In this case, the motion of the satellite is normal to the direction of gravitational pull at all times. As the satellite moves forward, its path is curved by the pull of gravity. The resulting curvature of its path is precisely the amount needed to keep it at a constant distance from the center of gravity of the body about which it is orbiting. Since it is always pulled by the gravitational attraction in a direction normal to its motion, it neither gains nor loses velocity in response to the pull of gravity. At all points in the orbit, therefore, the satellite is moving at the same velocity and is the same distance from the center of gravity.

The circular orbit is a unique orbit, the elliptical (or eccentric) orbit is the general case. The relationship between a circular orbit and an elliptical orbit may be understood by studying the changes that take place in the orbit when a satellite that is initially in a circular orbit makes a velocity change. Several very simple velocity maneuvers are illustrated in Figures 4-2 through 4-5. In all these maneuvers, a velocity change of ten percent of the satellite's initial orbital velocity is applied. This velocity change is added vectorially in a different manner in each example shown. In Figure 4-2, the velocity is

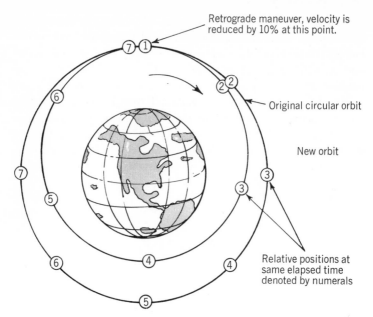

Fig. 4-2.   The modification of a circular orbit by a propulsive maneuver that reduces the forward velocity by 10 percent.

added in a retrograde (backward) direction so that the satellite is slowed to 90 percent of its initial velocity. In Figure 4-3,
the velocity was applied in the posigrad (forward) direction
and the satellite was speeded up to 110 percent of its initial
velocity. In Figure 4-4, the velocity change vector was applied
inwardly so that the forward velocity remained unchanged but
the direction of flight was deflected inwardly. In Figure 4-5,
the velocity vector was applied laterally so that the foward
velocity was again left unchanged, but the orbit was deflected
into another plane.

In the case where the maneuver reduced the forward velocity, the satellite was left with insufficient energy to maintain
the initial altitude of the circular orbit. Its flight path therefore
curves more sharply and it loses altitude. As a consequence, its
path is soon going "down hill" and the pull of gravity begins
accelerating its motion along the new orbital path. The path

continues to get steeper until enough forward velocity is achieved so that the curvature of the flight path gets great enough to prevent further steepening of the downhill tendency. This happens approximately 90° from the point at which the retarding maneuver was made. However, the path is still down hill and the satellite's velocity continues to increase. The pull of gravity has been getting stronger and the curvature of the path starts to increase, but as it approaches the center of gravity of the parent mass, the curvature of its path becomes increasingly greater than the path curvature for constant rate of descent. Consequently, the rate of descent decreases. At 180° from the starting point, the rate of descent is zero and the satellite is no longer increasing its velocity. At this time, it is traveling at the maximum velocity for the new orbit. This is the point of *perigee*. It is traveling much faster than the velocity it had initially while in circular orbit. Since it is going overspeed, the curvature of its path is not great enough to prevent it from gaining altitude. Consequently, it gains altitude at an increasing rate for the next 90° and then at a decreasing rate for the following 90° until it is once more at the starting point, which is the *apogee*. The path from perigee back to the starting point is a mirror image of the path from the starting point to perigee.

The apogee is the point of highest altitude and the point of lowest velocity in an orbit. And perigee is the point of lowest altitude and greatest velocity. At both apogee and perigee, the path is exactly normal to the pull of gravity and altitude is neither increasing nor decreasing. Between apogee and perigee, however, altitude is lost and the velocity increases. Between perigee and apogee, altitude is gained and the velocity decreases.

A satellite in orbit has both kinetic energy and potential energy. The kinetic energy is energy that is contained within the satellite due to its velocity and represents the work that would be required in order to create the velocity it has. The potential energy is the energy in the satellite associated with its altitude and represents the work that would be needed to lift it to that altitude from a reference altitude.

The satellite's kinetic energy and potential energy are constantly being exchanged. At apogee, the kinetic energy is at its lowest level and the potential energy is at its peak. While moving to the perigee point, some of the potential energy gets converted into kinetic energy. At perigee, the kinetic energy is at its peak and the potential energy is at its lowest level. At all times, however, the sum of the kinetic energy and potential energy remains constant.

In Figure 4-2, the relative position of the satellite in the new orbit, and the position it would have had if it had not undergone velocity change, are illustrated. It will be noticed that although the initial maneuver was to retard the satellite's for-

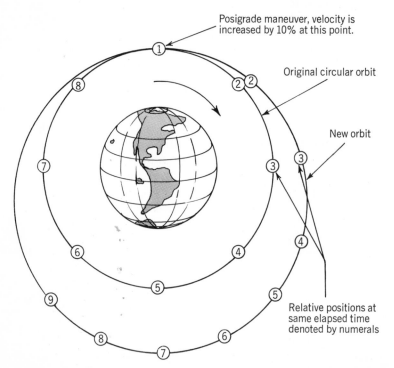

Fig. 4-3. The modification of a circular orbit by a propulsive maneuver that increases the forward velocity by 10 percent.

ward motion, it completes the orbit in less time than it would have taken in the original circular orbit. This is a result of the fact that the average velocity in the new orbit is greater than in the original orbit and also because the distance around the new orbit is less.

The maneuver illustrated in Figure 4-3 is exactly the opposite of the one just described. In this case, the velocity is increased and the starting point of the new orbit becomes its perigee. The new orbit is larger than the original circular orbit and its period is longer.

In the maneuver shown in Figure 4-4, an inward velocity vector is added to the initial velocity. In this case, the forward velocity is initially unchanged, but the path has been abruptly changed into the "down hill" direction. Although the orbit has

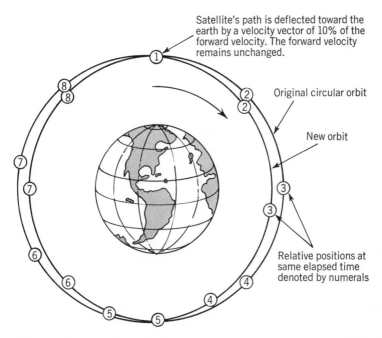

Fig. 4-4. The modification of a circular orbit by a propulsive maneuver that deflects the path toward the earth.

been made elliptical, it has the same energy as the original circular orbit, since the particular maneuver did not immediately change its absolute velocity nor its altitude. A consequence of this is that the period of the new orbit is the same as that of the original orbit. Since the path is initially downhill, the satellite in its new orbit will start to gain velocity. After traveling about 90°, it reaches its perigee and after traveling about 180°, it is back to its initial altitude. It is also back to its initial velocity. It is ahead of the position it would have had if it had remained in its initial orbit, since it has been averaging a faster velocity over a shorter path during the interval. The next 180° are traveled at an average velocity that is lower than that for the circular orbit, since it is at higher altitudes and the energy balance demands a lower velocity. After passing the apogee point, it descends to the starting point and arrives there at the same instant that it would have if it had remained in the original circular orbit. The original orbit and the new orbit are therefore called *synchronous,* or *equi-period orbits* since they require the same time to complete one revolution.

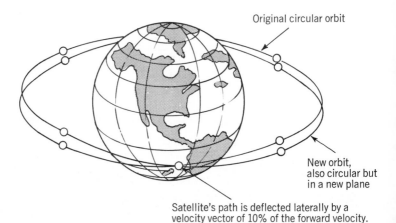

Original circular orbit

New orbit, also circular but in a new plane

Satellite's path is deflected laterally by a velocity vector of 10% of the forward velocity. The forward velocity remains unchanged.

Fig. 4-5.   The modification of a circular orbit by a propulsive maneuver that deflects the path laterally.

The orbital maneuvers just described and illustrated in Figure 4-2, 4-3, and 4-4 are all maneuvers that were carried out within the plane of the original orbit. Therefore, they can be illustrated in a two-dimensional figure. There are also maneuvers that carry the satellite out of its initial orbital plane. The simplest such maneuver would be one wherein an impulse is applied directly across the orbital path. Such a maneuver is shown in Figure 4-5. In this case, the added velocity vector neither changes the forward velocity nor does it turn the path toward or away from the center of gravity. The result is to put the satellite into another circular orbit that is synchronous with, but in a different plane from the original one. It can be seen that the two orbits coincide at the starting point and at a point every 180° from the starting point.

The orbital maneuvers discussed are all special cases, since the velocity which was added was limited to only the lateral, vertical, or longitudinal directions. Obviously, velocity may be added in any combination of these directions. In such cases, the orbit will be changed in a related combination of those illustrated.

Rendezvous

Now that a few of the fundamentals of orbital mechanics have been shown, the practical application of orbital maneuvers for rendezvous of the Gemini spacecraft with the Agena can be discussed. The Agena target vehicle is first placed into an orbit about the Earth. Since the Earth is rotating, the launch site at Cape Kennedy can be expected to pass below the orbit of the target vehicle once or twice a day. At such times, the Gemini spacecraft could be launched from the Cape into an orbit nearly the same as the one occupied by the target vehicle. Unless the Gemini were launched at a precise time, it could not be guided into the same position in the orbit occupied by the target vehicle. Every second of error in launching time would result in a five-mile position error. It is not yet considered operationally practical to depend upon launching a spacecraft with less than one hour tolerance in time. Thus, it

is obvious that maneuvers subsequent to launching are required to bring the Gemini to the location of the Agena target
vehicle.

One procedure is to launch the Gemini into an orbit
that is at a lower altitude than the target vehicle orbit. The
Gemini will then be in a shorter period orbit than that of the
target vehicle. Such an orbit is called a *catch-up* orbit, since
the Gemini will be traveling faster than the target vehicle and
will overtake it periodically.

The transfer maneuver that will move the Gemini into the
target vehicle's orbit is fairly simple. The Gemini first makes a
speed-up maneuver which places it into an eccentric orbit

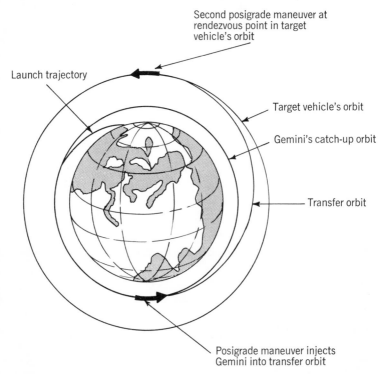

Fig. 4-6. Maneuvers employed by Gemini to rendezvous with the
Agena target vehicle.

(the transfer orbit) with an apogee at the same altitude as the orbit of the target vehicle. When the Gemini spacecraft arrives at its apogee, it must make another speed-up maneuver to make its orbit circular. In order for the transfer maneuver to be accurate, the velocity added must be precisely controlled and executed at the right time. The timing, however, is not nearly as critical as the launch timing, since the relative velocity between the Gemini and the target vehicle will be a small portion of their orbital velocity. The rendezvous maneuvers are illustrated in Figure 4-6.

The maneuver described will place the Gemini in the near vicinity (visual or radar range) of the target, with highly efficient utilization of propellants. The final closing and docking maneuvers are carried out subsequent to visual or radar contact. These maneuvers are carried out under the direct control of the crew, whereas the orbit transfer maneuvers are directed by the guidance computer.

Lunar Missions

Since the moon is in orbit about the Earth, a flight to the moon is in many ways similar to the rendezvous maneuver just described. The mission is started from an orbit about the Earth. The departure maneuver is illustrated in Figure 4-7. The spacecraft is accelerated to a velocity approximately 40 percent in excess of orbital velocity. This maneuver is made at a point in orbit almost diametrically opposite to the predicted position of the moon at the expected arrival time. Thus, immediately after the maneuver, the spacecraft is not headed for the moon, but for a position which is about 150° behind the moon in its orbit. The pull of the earth's gravity will curve the path of the spacecraft so that it is soon heading for a point ahead of the moon in its orbit. However, when the moon's gravity becomes effective in dominating the motion of the spacecraft, it curves the flight of the spacecraft toward it. This is shown in Figure 4-8. The relative position of the Earth, the moon, and the spacecraft are not exactly as shown because the motion of the moon in its orbit is not accounted for.

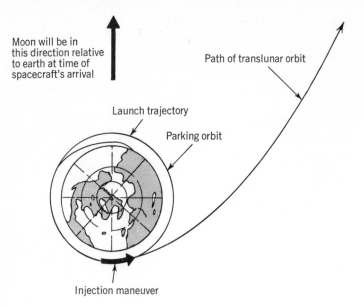

Moon will be in
this direction relative
to earth at time of
spacecraft's arrival

Path of translunar orbit

Launch trajectory

Parking orbit

Injection maneuver

Fig. 4-7.   Injection into translunar orbit from parking orbit.

As the spacecraft approaches the moon, its motion becomes almost completely dominated by the moon's gravitational field. Then, the fact that the moon is orbiting about the earth can be overlooked, since only the relative motion between the spacecraft and moon are important. The point of closest approach

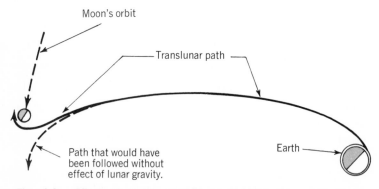

Moon's orbit

Translunar path

Path that would have
been followed without
effect of lunar gravity.

Earth

Fig. 4-8.   Effect of lunar gravitational field as the moon is approached. (This is not drawn to scale.)

to the moon is called *pericynthian*. At this time, the spacecraft will be on the opposite side of the moon from the Earth. This is the position at which the spacecraft will have to decelerate to be captured into a lunar orbit. This is often referred to as the *de-boost maneuver*. The descent from lunar orbit is a propulsive maneuver which has been described in Chapter 2. In returning to earth, the spacecraft will depart from lunar orbit on the side opposite from the Earth in a maneuver similar to the departure from Earth orbit.

The return flight to the Earth will be along a path similar to the outbound leg. At a short distance from the moon, the spacecraft's motion will once again be dominated by the Earth's gravity. The perigee point of the return orbit is within the Earth's atmosphere. Thus, this return path carries the spacecraft into the reentry maneuver.

At lunar-return velocity, the path angle at which the spacecraft reenters the atmosphere must be held within a very close tolerance. Too steep a path will cause excessive aerodynamic deceleration loads upon the crew; if the path is too shallow, the spacecraft may skip back out of the atmosphere. The perigee point of the returning spacecraft must lie within a 20-mile spread in altitude, otherwise it will be unable to negotiate a safe reentry.

Escape Maneuvers

In returning from the moon, the spacecraft must be accelerated to a velocity greater than "escape velocity." Escape velocity is the velocity required to depart the gravitational field of an astronomical body. It is also the velocity that a particle will have if it fell from an initial velocity of zero at an infinite distance toward such a body (free from disturbances from other gravitational fields). It can therefore be seen that escape velocity is a function of the distance to the astronomical body and its mass. The proportionality is simply expressed:

$$V_e^2 = K \frac{M}{D}$$

where v_e = escape velocity, M = mass of astronomical body, D = distance from centers, and K = constant of proportionality.

If a particle has greater than escape velocity, it has sufficient energy to free itself from the gravitational field of a planet (or other astrononomical body). If it has less than escape velocity, it is a captive of the planet and therefore it is a satellite of the planet.

If its velocity is exactly equal to escape velocity, it will be on a parabolic path. The focus point of the parabolic path will be the center of mass of the planet. Escape velocity is therefore sometimes called *parabolic velocity*. At velocities greater than escape velocity, the motion of the particle will trace a hyperbolic curve, and the particle may be said to have *hyperbolic velocity*.

It should be obvious that a particle at escape velocity will be constantly undergoing a change in velocity. However, since its distance from the planet also changes, the condition of being at escape velocity persists. Figure 4-9 shows several paths for particles at escape velocity. Note that all particles are traveling at the same speed when they are at the same distance from the center of mass.

When a satellite is in a circular orbit, it has one-half the

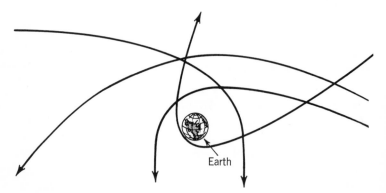

Fig. 4-9.   Paths of objects at escape velocity.

kinetic energy needed for escape. Thus, for a given distance from the center of mass of a planet, the following relation holds:

$$V_e = \sqrt{2}\, V_c$$

where V_e = velocity of escape and V_c = velocity of a circular orbit.

A spacecraft must increase its velocity to greater than escape velocity if it is to depart the Earth's gravitational influence for an interplanetary trip. As it leaves the Earth, it will lose velocity, since it will be traveling against the pull of gravity. The final velocity it will retain as it approaches the practical limit of the Earth's gravitational influence is simply the velocity associated with the excess of kinetic energy over the kinetic energy of escape. Thus, since kinetic energy is proportional to the velocity squared:

$$V^2 = V_x^{\,2} - V_e^{\,2}$$

where V = departure velocity, V_x = velocity at x distance from earth, and V_e = escape velocity at x.

The velocity remaining at an infinite distance from earth is herein defined as the *departure velocity*. It is almost always important to achieve the desired departure velocity with the least propulsive effort. Since the departure velocity will depend upon the total energy stored in the spacecraft, the desirable thing to do is to increase the spacecraft's energy to the required level with the least amount of additional velocity. Thus, an escape maneuver is best carried out by accelerating along the initial direction of travel. An orbiting spacecraft is at its greatest velocity at perigee. By accelerating the spacecraft in the region of perigee, the least amount of additional velocity will be required to achieve the desired departure velocity. This is because the amount of energy added to the spacecraft per increment of velocity increase is proportional to its existing velocity.

Navigation

A fundamental problem in navigation is the determination
of one's position. Many of the principles of marine navigation
are applicable to space navigation. In marine navigation the
determination of one's position is a straightforward problem
in geometry, provided landmarks are visible. A bearing is
taken on the landmarks by measuring their direction relative
to north. This may be done with a sighting device, such as a
pelorus, mounted on deck. The observed bearings are converted to an angle measured clockwise from true north. These
"true bearings" are then plotted as lines on the navigator's
chart. Where the bearing lines cross on the chart is the location that was occupied by the ship at the time the sightings
were made.

For example, if a navigator on a ship measured the true
bearings of a lighthouse at 320°, and of a water tower at 230°,
he would then plot them on his chart as shown in Figure 4-10.
Where these lines cross is his location, called a *fix*. In plotting
such a fix, it is presumed that the bearings are made simultaneously or that the ship has traveled only a negligible
distance between sightings.

If the ship is moving rapidly and some time elapses between
the bearings, the navigator may still determine his position,

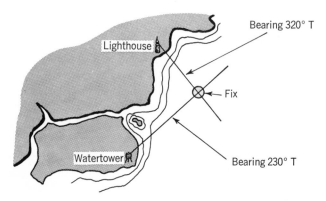

Fig. 4-10.   Fix obtained from simultaneous bearings on two landmarks.

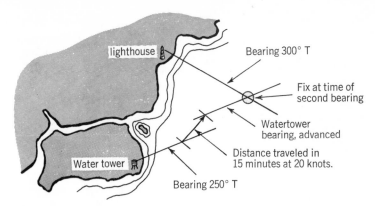

Fig. 4-11. Running fix obtained from bearings on two landmarks taken at a fifteen-minute interval.

provided he can approximate the distance and direction that the ship has traveled between the two measurements. Such a fix is called a *running fix*. For instance, if the ship is traveling on course 045° at 20 knots and a true bearing on the lighthouse of 300° is measured 15 minutes after a true bearing on the water tower of 250° is obtained, then a running fix would be plotted as shown on Figure 4-11.

First, the water tower bearing of 250° would be plotted. Then at a distance of four nautical miles to the northeast of this line, a line parallel to it is plotted. This is called "advancing" the bearing. Thus, these two lines are separated by the distance the ship has traveled between the times the two bearings are taken. The bearing on the lighthouse is then plotted on the chart. Where it and the advanced water-tower bearing cross is the position of the ship at the time the navigator took the bearing on the lighthouse.

If a navigator is very sure of his speed and direction of travel, he may use the running fix method to determine his position from only one landmark. In this case, he allows sufficient time to elapse between measurements so that the bearing on the landmark changes appreciably. Then he can plot the two bearings on his chart as shown in Figure 4-12.

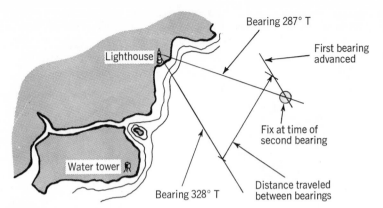

Fig. 4-12. Running fix from two bearings obtained from the same landmark.

The determination of position from measured bearings of known landmarks is the simplest form of marine navigation. When out of sight of landmarks, the navigator can determine his position from the location of the moon, the sun, and some of the planets and stars. This is done by sextant measurements of the elevation angles of these bodies above the horizon. Based upon the use of precomputed tables, the navigator can then determine the line of positions on the earth surface from which the measured elevation angle could be obtained. The crossing of two such lines obtained from sighting on two bodies is then his position. A navigator can also estimate his position by computing his direction and distance traveled since his last fix. This is called *dead reckoning.*

If a ship is equipped with radar, the navigator can determine his position by a radar observation of a single landmark. This is because both the range and the bearing of the landmark can be measured with the radar. Similarly, a radar ashore can determine the ship's position.

Besides needing to know his position, a navigator must also know the speed and direction in which his ship is traveling. Under ideal conditions, a ship can be expected to travel in the direction it is headed and at speed dependent only upon the number of revolutions its screw turns a minute. However, many things can modify its speed and direction, such as a dirty bottom, the load and trim of the ship, ocean currents, wind, and wave activity. For these reasons, the navigator measures his actual progress by measurements of distance and direction traveled between two fixes which he has plotted on his chart. He may then project these measured values of speed and heading to predict where he will be some time in the future. It should be pointed out that the accuracy of position determination is limited by the accuracy by which the measurements are made.

The important difference between marine navigation and space navigation is that the spacecraft is free to travel in three dimensions, whereas the ship which travels on the surface of the water is limited to movement on a surface. The general procedures of navigation are basically the same. However, the great speed of spacecraft requires that positions be determined quickly and accurately. The position of a spacecraft is determined from measured line of sights and possibly ranges to known reference points, the only difference being that angular measurements must be made in two reference planes instead of one. The speed and direction of travel can then be determined from the progress made from one measured position to the next.

A basic consideration is that a fix cannot be more accurate than the known position of the landmark or reference point. Since it is usually desirable to know the location of a spacecraft with an error no greater than a few miles, reference points with established positions of this accuracy must be used. There are several schemes that can be used which satisfy the accuracy requirements. The most direct is to use measured bearings and ranges from high-powered radar located at known positions on the earth. The Mercury network was equipped around the world with a number of radar stations that served this function. These were able to track the position of Mercury during its orbital flights. Instead of plotting the positions of the spacecraft on a chart, the tracking data was fed into a large digital computer which computed the position of the spacecraft from the tracking data. These computed positions were then recorded in the computer's memory. By making further computations based upon several recorded positions, the computer was able to determine the orbital path and speed of Mercury. An ephemeris of future orbits of the Mercury spacecraft was also computed from which such things as an accurate prediction of the expected landing point could be obtained.

In Apollo, ground tracking will also be used. Its reliability, when the Apollo spacecraft is as far away as the moon, may not be sufficient to serve as the sole means of navigation. For this reason, the Apollo carries accurate optical sighting equipment, a compact digital computer and an inertial platform. With this navigation equipment, Apollo can accurately navigate without assistance from the ground facilities.

Instead of carrying a great many charts, the Apollo will carry a microfilm file of a number of suitable landmarks on the Earth and the moon. The navigator can have these displayed on call at the navigation station. He can then note the position (latitude and longitude) of the chosen landmark and feed this to the computer through the key punch provided for instructing the computer. The computer's memory stores all the constants that are needed for computing the position of the earth and moon during the mission period. Also fixed in the memory of the computer is the position of a number of prominent celestial bodies. Thus the computer is not only able to make the requisite navigational computations, but it also carries all the basic information necessary to perform the computations. It is also equipped with a very accurate clock, since time is primary data for all navigation computations.

Navigation during the orbital portions of the mission is not too complicated, and since the distances to landmarks are not great, sufficient angular accuracy is relatively easy to obtain. For these cases, the sighting telescope is first used to determine the alignment of the inertial platform. It is aimed by the navigator at several stars in succession. When he has it accurately pointed at one of the navigation stars, he presses a "mark" button. The angular position of the telescope relative

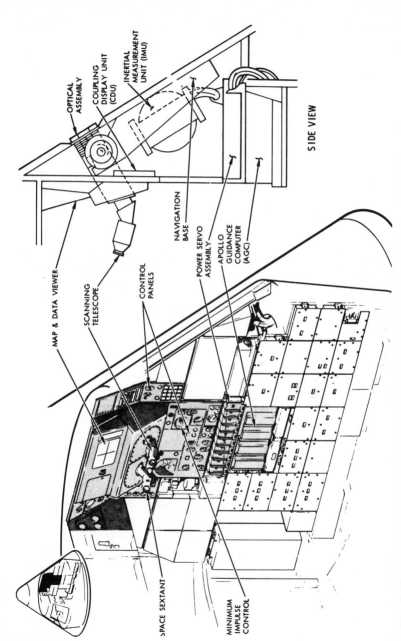

OPTICAL
ASSEMBLY

COUPLING
DISPLAY UNIT
(CDU)

INERTIAL
MEASUREMENT
UNIT (IMU)

NAVIGATION
BASE

POWER SERVO
ASSEMBLY

APOLLO
GUIDANCE
COMPUTER
(AGC)

SIDE VIEW

MAP & DATA VIEWER

SCANNING
TELESCOPE

CONTROL
PANELS

SPACE SEXTANT

MINIMUM
IMPULSE
CONTROL

Fig. 4-13.   Installation of command module guidance and navigation equipment. (NASA)

to the inertial platform is then automatically recorded by the computer. After several such star positions are fed into the computer, it "knows" how the inertial platform is aligned relative to the celestial sphere (inertial space). The computer is programmed so that it can make navigation computations with any arbitrary alignment of the platform, just as long as it has knowledge of what the alignment is. However, when maneuvers are to be made, there are preferred positions of alignment. In such cases, the computer can generate instructions that rotate the platform into the desired alignment.

When the alignment of the platform is established, the navigator is ready to determine his position. He does this by sighting landmarks on the surface of the moon (assuming he is in lunar orbit). He sends a "mark" signal to the computer at the exact instant the telescope is aimed at a particular landmark. The computer, by referring the pointing position of the telescope to the inertial platform position, is able to determine the angular direction of the landmark from the spacecraft relative to inertial space. Since the spacecraft is moving so fast, no attempt is made to obtain a fix from simultaneous measurements on two landmarks. The computer takes into account the motion of spacecraft between sightings and determines the spacecraft position in a manner similar to a running fix in marine navigation. However, since the same sightings may be used to determine the direction and velocity of motion, the computing procedure is a little more complex. Actually, the computer searches for the orbit that best matches the series of sightings of landmarks on the lunar surface.

When the Apollo is in flight between the Earth and moon, the distance to the landmarks is so great that extremely accurate angular measurements of their position must be made. The angular accuracy of neither the platform nor the telescope is sufficient for these measurements. For this reason, Apollo carries a space sextant. This instrument minimizes the measurement errors of landmark position by using a high-powered split-optical system. With the sextant, the navigator superimposes the image of one of the navigation stars upon a landmark. At the exact instant of superposition, the navigator

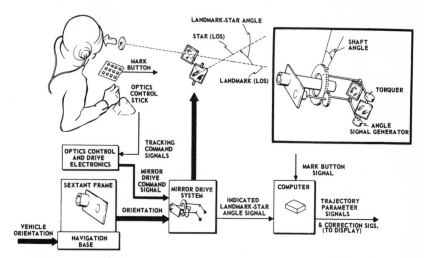

Fig. 4-14. Functional and schematic diagrams of the Apollo sextant.
(NASA)

sends a mark signal to the computer. The angle between the
position of the star and the landmark establishes the position
of the spacecraft on the surface of an imaginary cone that has
its apex at the landmark. The axis of the cone extends from
the landmark to the star that was sighted. The half-angle of
the cone is the measured angle between the star and the landmark or its supplement. This is illustrated by the drawing in
Figure 4-15.

The computer has stored information on the position of the
landmark and the star. Therefore, the measurement of their
subtended angle provides the necessary information for the
computer to establish the "surface of positions" on which the
spacecraft must lie. When the navigator makes another sextant
measurement on a second star, but with the same landmark,
the computer can determine another surface of positions for
the spacecraft. The intersection of these surfaces creates a line
of position, which can be most accurately established if the
plane of measurement for the second star is nearly perpendicular to that of the first.

In order to get a fix, the navigator must use an additional

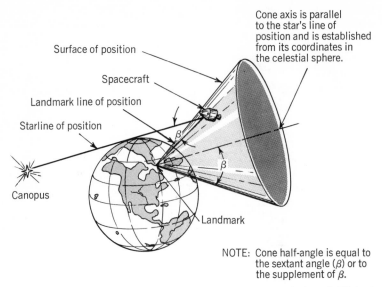

Surface of position

Spacecraft

Landmark line of position

Starline of position

Cone axis is parallel
to the star's line of
position and is established
from its coordinates in
the celestial sphere.

Canopus

Landmark

NOTE: Cone half-angle is equal to
the sextant angle (β) or to
the supplement of β.

Fig. 4-15. The surface of position of the spacecraft is established
from the measured sextant angle, the location of the landmark, and
the position of the star on the celestial sphere.

landmark. This will establish a third conical surface of position, intersected by the established line of position. Again, it is
desirable to have the angle of intersection between line and
surface as large as possible. For this reason, the landmark used
in the last sighting should be on the moon if the first landmark
was on the Earth, and vice versa.

Although the several sightings were described as all being
made at the same instant, obviously this could not happen.
Once again, the computer is programmed to evaluate the
effect of the velocity and direction of motion to make a running fix.

The determination of position in space is only a part of the
navigation task. The computer must also determine the velocity and direction of travel of the spacecraft. This can be done
by the comparison of a series of fixes. The gravitational attraction of the Earth and moon must be accounted for in this

process since gravitational fields will bend the path along which the spacecraft is traveling, and will cause the velocity to change. The next step is to predict the spacecraft's position at future times. The predicted position is then compared with a "target" position for the particular leg of the journey. For instance, when the spacecraft is outbound for the moon, the target position is the planned location of pericynthian. If the calculated position of pericynthian is different than the desired one, then the path must be corrected. The computer not only determines such errors, but also computes the requisite corrective maneuver. Such maneuvers are called *mid-course guidance maneuvers.*

Guidance

A mid-course guidance maneuver consists of the following events. First, the spacecraft's attitude is rotated to the desired one. The reaction control jets are used to turn the spacecraft. The inertial measuring unit is used to indicate the desired attitude. When the spacecraft propulsion axis is pointed in the direction desired, the main propulsion engine is started and accelerates the spacecraft in the direction necessary to eliminate the computed error. The inertial measuring unit in conjunction with the computer integrates the change taking place in the spacecraft's velocity. At the instant the computed error is nullified, the computer sends a cut-off signal to the propulsion system.

The mid-course maneuvers are of small velocity magnitude and take place at fairly great distances from either the Earth or the moon. These maneuvers are therefore carried out with the spacecraft on a constant heading. For other propulsive maneuvers, requiring a large change in velocity such as the de-boost maneuver into lunar orbit, the direction along which the thrust should be applied changes during the period of the maneuver. This is so, because, as the spacecraft moves in the vicinity of the moon, its flight path curves and the direction of pull from lunar gravity also changes. The computer is programmed to guide the spacecraft through this maneuver.

The computer on the command module makes two other major guidance maneuvers. One, the departure from lunar orbit, is quite similar to the de-boost maneuver. The other, reentry in the Earth's atmosphere, is different in that it involves the control of aerodynamic lift and drag, rather than propulsive thrust. The manner in which this control is exercised is described in Chapter 8.

The LEM has a guidance and navigation system quite similar to that of the command module. The exception is in the optical system. Since the LEM only operates in the immediate vicinity of the moon, it is not as difficult to navigate the LEM. Therefore, the LEM does not carry a sextant but instead employs a small telescope to maintain alignment of its inertial measuring unit.

The LEM's descent to the surface of the moon is guided by the computer based upon deceleration measurements made by the inertial measuring unit. During such maneuvers, the computer continually integrates the deceleration along each orthagonal axis of the inertial measuring unit. This integration process, which takes into account the lunar gravitational pull, provides the computer with continuous knowledge of the spacecraft's velocity and direction of travel. The velocity is also continually integrated to provide a continuous location of the spacecraft position. It should be noted that the position so obtained is based upon computed progress from a measured starting point. Thus, the computer would be guiding the spacecraft to the landing point by dead reckoning. As the spacecraft approaches the moon's surface, its altitude will be measured by the landing radar. This altitude measurement is also fed to the computer to correct the altitude obtained by the dead-reckoning method. The computer is programmed to bring the LEM's horizontal velocity to stop a few hundred feet above the surface of the moon. It will then slowly descend to a complete stop a few feet above the surface of the moon. At this position, a cut-off signal will be sent to the propulsion system and the LEM will drop in lunar gravity to a landing. During the final phases, the astronauts can interrupt the programmed landing maneuver and move the landing point to a more desirable location. When the astronaut discontinues overriding the controls, the LEM computer once again resumes the vertical descent maneuver, this time over the new location.

The LEM computer also guides the LEM through the subsequent launch maneuver that leads to rendezvous with the command and service module. The guidance during launch is similar to a launch from the earth. The orbit into which the LEM is launched is one that leads to a meeting with the command module in its orbit.

As the LEM sits on the surface of the moon in preparation for launch, the desired LEM orbit for rendezvous is constantly changing, since the position of the command module is constantly progressing along its orbital path. The LEM computer has the ephemeris of the command module stored within it, so that it is able to generate the requisite guidance instruction for the proper launch maneuver. After the LEM is launched into orbit, it may go as far as half-way around the moon before it approaches the command module. It is expected that the guidance errors encountered during launch will result in the LEM being placed in an orbit that will miss the command module by several miles. For this reason, the LEM will be expected to make one or more mid-course maneuvers as it approaches the command module. These maneuvers will be made on the basis of updated position information obtained from radar or optical measurements of the target. The command module will also be able to track the LEM and assist it in this phase. The final closing maneuver is carried out by the crew in a manner similar to that employed in Gemini's rendezvous with the Agena.

5

Providing for the Crew

All of the necessities of life must be considered in the design of a spacecraft. Not only must food and water be carried, but a cabin atmosphere must be maintained that is healthy and comfortable. There is also a requirement for the sanitary disposal of garbage and human waste. Although these seem to be everyday problems, dealt with almost casually on earth, they become rather formidable in the environment of space.

The occupants of a spacecraft also require special physical support to assist them in tolerating the launch and reentry phases of space flight. This chapter is a discussion of the provisions aboard a spacecraft that are associated with the physical needs of the crew.

Spacecraft Atmospheric Requirements

The atmosphere on Earth is a mixture of 80 percent nitrogen and 20 percent oxygen, with minor quantities of water vapor and carbon dioxide. There are also traces of other gases which are not important to this discussion. The oxygen in the atmosphere is essential to life. If the oxygen were removed from the air we breathe, we would become unconscious almost immediately and would die in a few minutes. Since the human body is continually consuming oxygen, a spacecraft must be equipped to continually replenish the oxygen in the cabin as it is used.

The nitrogen in the Earth's atmosphere does not appear to have any direct importance to animal life. However, life has evolved to accommodate an atmosphere in which the vital oxygen has been diluted with nitrogen. It has been found that undiluted oxygen at sea level pressure can be toxic if exposure lasts as long as a day. The toxic effects generally diminish when the pressure is reduced. In fact, when pure oxygen is breathed at a pressure nearly the same as the partial pressure of oxygen in a normal sea level atmosphere, there are no detectable toxic effects. For this reason, an atmosphere of almost pure oxygen at five pounds per square inch was chosen for Mercury, Gemini, and Apollo. This is slightly above the sea level partial pressure (3.5 psi). Although a pure oxygen atmosphere at such pressures does not appear to be toxic, it has been conjectured that an exposure duration exceeding a few weeks may be harmful.

The amount of water vapor in the atmosphere is termed *humidity*. Humidity is highly variable in the atmosphere of the Earth. Consequently, animal life is highly tolerant to wide extremes in humidity. Humidity control is important, however, since neither extremely high nor extremely low levels of humidity are conducive to comfort and health. Since water vapor is continuously expelled through respiration by the crew, a manned spacecraft must have equipment to condense and remove it from the cabin atmosphere.

A small amount of carbon dioxide such as found to exist naturally in the Earth's atmosphere is harmless. However, carbon dioxide is a toxic substance and when its concentration increases appreciably above the natural level, it can produce harmful effects. This is very important, since carbon dioxide is produced by the body's metabolism and subsequently released to the lungs to be exhaled into the atmosphere. It is important, therefore, to continuously remove carbon dioxide from the atmosphere of a manned spacecraft in a manner that will keep its concentration very low.

It can be seen from the foregoing discussion that manned spacecraft must have an active system to maintain a healthy atmosphere in the cabin. This system should replenish the oxygen that the crew consumes, remove water vapor and carbon dioxide that the crew produces, and maintain the temperature in the cabin at a comfortable level. If the crew is expected to live in the spacecraft for periods exceeding a few weeks, then the cabin atmosphere should also contain a diluent gas such as nitrogen. The environmental control system must then be equipped to control the supply of this additional gas in a manner to maintain the desired proportions of oxygen and nitrogen.

The inclusion of nitrogen in a spacecraft is not done without penalties. Since nitrogen and oxygen are both odorless, it is not possible for the crew to sense the concentrations of oxygen in the air they breathe. Yet if the partial pressure of oxygen falls below 2.5 psi, the crew is in serious danger of slipping into an unconscious state. The crew must therefore rely on instruments to tell them that the atmosphere is being maintained in a safe balance. Measurements of the partial pressure of these gases can only be made with relatively complex instrumentation.

Environmental Control System

The machinery that maintains the atmosphere aboard a spacecraft is called the *environmental control system*. This system regulates the cabin pressure and temperature, removes moisture, carbon dioxide, and odors, and circulates the atmosphere through the cabin and/or the crew's space suits.

Oxygen Supply

The supply of oxygen for a spacecraft can be carried either as a high pressure gas, as a cryogenic fluid, or chemically combined with other elements, as a solid. While storage as a high pressure gas is the simplest, it is also the heaviest method. A fully loaded high pressure oxygen storage bottle is heavier than the oxygen which it contains.

Liquid oxygen can be stored in much lighter and smaller tanks than are required for gaseous storage. There are, however, several difficulties associated with the use of liquid storage for oxygen. To start with, the oxygen must be kept below $-297°F$. This requires special thermal insulation. If excessive heat leaks into the liquid oxygen container, it will boil and the pressure in the container will rise. In this case,

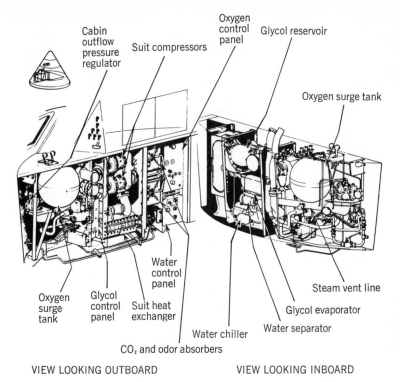

Fig. 5-1. Installation of environmental control equipment in Apollo command module. (NASA)

some of the oxygen must be discharged (and presumably wasted); otherwise, the storage vessel would rupture. Another difficulty lies in the fact that the storage vessel would not contain just liquid oxygen, but would be partly filled with gaseous oxygen. As a matter of fact, as oxygen is removed, the volume occupied by liquid oxygen will decrease, while the volume of gaseous oxygen increases. A serious difficulty lies in controlling the type of fluid (liquid or gas) to be removed from the vessel. Ordinarily, it is desired to remove oxygen as a gas. This is because the gas is in a higher energy state and will carry away more heat energy from the storage vessel as it is discharged. Thus, a greater amount of heat leaking into the vessel may be accommodated. But it is difficult to construct a storage tank that will faithfully discharge gaseous instead of liquid oxygen in a state of weightlessness. There is one final consideration. This has to do with maintaining an adequate pressure within the vessel. As the oxygen is being consumed, the pressure inside the vessel drops. The amount of heat leaking into the vessel usually will not be sufficient to maintain an adequate discharge pressure. For this reason, an electric heater must be placed inside the vessel. By heating the oxygen from time to time, the desired storage pressure can be maintained.

Some of the problems associated with liquid oxygen storage are avoided by "super-critical storage" of oxygen. A super-critical fluid is a fluid in a physical state between the liquid and gaseous states. In the super-critical state, oxygen is nearly as dense as liquid oxygen, yet it acts like a compressible fluid. (That is, it will expand or contract with variations in pressure or temperature.) The advantage of using super-critical storage lies in the fact that the fluid exists in only one state inside the storage vessel and, as a result, there is no uncertainty as to what will be discharged from the tank in the weightless environment.

Oxygen exists in the super-critical phase at temperatures slightly above $-182°F$ and pressures above 746 psi. A super-critical storage system is somewhat heavier than a liquid storage system, since the higher pressures involved require stronger storage vessels. However, super-critical storage is still much lighter than high pressure gas storage. The super-critical system must also use electric heaters to maintain storage pressure as oxygen is consumed. Both Gemini and Apollo carry oxygen stored as a super-critical fluid. Since oxygen must be stored for some time prior to launch, the storage bottles are vacuum-jacketed to maintain a high level of thermal insulation. Incongruous as it may seem, these spacecraft are carrying a vacuum into space.

CO_2 and H_2O Removal

The oxygen consumed by the crew reacts chemically with food and thereby produces energy. The ultimate waste products of this chemical reaction are carbon dioxide and water. Nearly all of the carbon dioxide produced is expelled into the air through respiration. An individual may be expected to consume about 2.1 pounds of carbon dioxide in the process. He will also produce about half a pound of metabolic water; but this amount of water is a small consideration in comparison to the total amount of water the body gains and loses during the day. His total water intake also includes the water he drinks and the water contained in the food he eats. He loses water through perspiration, by his respiratory action, through urination, and in fecal waste. The total water intake will vary greatly, but will normally be in excess of five pounds per day. Over a period of time, an individual will lose the same amount of water as his water intake. Thus, his average daily water losses equal his average daily intake. However, on any given day, the amount of losses and gains in water should not be expected to be the same. The total amount and manner in which an individual may lose water during a day will depend upon his level of activity and the temperature and humidity of the atmosphere. The amounts that are lost by perspiration and respiratory action are particularly important to the design of the environmental control system. During a typical day, an individual may lose two or three pounds of water into the atmosphere. However, if the individual is very active and in a warm environment, he may lose several pounds of water in a single hour.

The carbon dioxide and water put into the atmosphere by the crew must be removed by the environmental control system. Water is easily removed by condensation on a cool surface. Carbon dioxide is much more difficult to remove. There are a number of methods of removing carbon dioxide. The method used in Mercury, Gemini, and Apollo is by use of lithium hydroxide. Carbon dioxide combines with lithium hydroxide in accordance with the following reaction:

$$CO_2 + 2LiOH \longrightarrow Li_2CO_3 + H_2O$$

About two and a half pounds of lithium hydroxide must be

carried per man per day. For short missions such as those mentioned, lithium hydroxide is the lightest method of carbon dioxide removal. For longer missions, it is desirable to use a method that does not require a consumable substance. For this reason, regenerative systems for carbon dioxide removal are being developed for use in long duration spacecraft.

A typical regenerative carbon dioxide removal system employs a molecular sieve. This is a bed of specially processed zeolite that will absorb carbon dioxide from the air passed through it. Several such beds would be carried. While one or more beds would be active in carbon dioxide absorption, the other beds could be isolated from the cabin atmosphere and desorbed. The desorbtion process may be carried out by simply venting the bed to the vacuum of space. If it is desirable to salvage the carbon dioxide from the molecular sieve, it may be desorbed by the application of heat.

Oxygen Regeneration

On very long spacecraft missions, such as flights to nearby planets, considerable weight can be saved in consumable stores if oxygen is regenerated from recovered water and carbon dioxide. This may be done if the energy required for the regenerative process does not in itself use consumables. However, solar or nuclear energy sources are almost certain to be used on such long duration flights. While biological gardens have been studied for regeneration of oxygen, they are not nearly as compact and efficient as process machinery.

The reclamation of oxygen from water is most simply done by electrolysis. A by-product of this process is hydrogen. The hydrogen may be used to replenish the hydrogen expended in the reclamation of oxygen from carbon dioxide. It should be noted that only a small portion of the water recovered will be available for oxygen reclamation, since water is also needed for drinking and reconstitution of dry food.

The reclamation of oxygen from carbon dioxide is somewhat difficult. One of the schemes is the catalytic combination of carbon dioxide and hydrogen to form methane and water:

$$CO_2 + 4H_2 \longrightarrow CH_4 + 2H_2O$$

The hydrogen would then be recovered from the methane and reused in the initial reaction with more carbon dioxide.

Atmosphere Contaminants

Since a spacecraft uses the same atmosphere over and over again by replenishing the oxygen and removing water and carbon dioxide, contaminants entering the cabin atmosphere will remain. The sources for these contaminants are the same on a spacecraft as those found on Earth. On Earth, however, there is almost always sufficient ventilation so that such contaminants are ignored or cause only temporary discomfort. In a spacecraft, the concentration of such contaminants may slowly increase to the point that they are not only noxious, but present a danger to the life of the crew. Spacecraft atmosphere contaminants may include the products of decomposition from aging or overheated non-metallic materials, flatus from the crew, and leakage from plumbing or equipment that may contain undesirable liquids and gases.

The contaminants to be dealt with are aerosols and gases. The aerosols are most easily removed by filtration. A great many of the gases are easily removed by absorption with activated charcoal. Activated charcoal can be expected to remove all of the gaseous contaminants that might be expected to occur with the exception of methane, hydrogen, and carbon monoxide. Unfortunately, minor concentration of these gases are explosive as well as toxic. Their removal can be accomplished by use of a catalytic burner. Such a device will oxidize them into water and carbon dioxide, which in turn would be removed by the other equipment.

Water and Food

A greater weight of water is needed daily by the crew than any other consumable. Therefore, an adequate supply of water is a primary consideration in planning a spacecraft. Water is needed for drinking, to reconstitute food, and for personal hygiene. On Mercury, sufficient water was carried in special storage tanks for the use of the crew. In Apollo and Gemini, the fuel cells manufacture an adequate supply of water as a by-product of power production. In space missions of long duration, the fuel cell is impractical for power production. In this case it becomes important to consider recovery and reuse of a modest initial amount of stored water to save weight. As explained previously, condensation of water vapor in the cabin atmosphere is one of the normal functions of the environmental control system. Additional water may be recovered from wash water and urine, by the provision of additional processing equipment for this purpose. Water may also be obtained from solid waste, but the special equipment required for processing make the weight saving dubious. There are several processes that may be used for water reclamation from liquid waste, but it appears that a distillation process may be the most practical. Laboratory tests of prototype water recovery systems have shown that sterilization of the recovered water is desirable. This may be done with heat, ultraviolet light, or chemicals.

Experience has shown that while men can function efficiently on a diet of concentrated, unappealing food, good meals are a prime factor in maintaining morale. Therefore, it is desirable to offer spacecraft crews the best diet practical within the constraints of the allowable volume for food storage. Freeze-dried food is ideally suited for space missions in every respect except its bulk. It is light, easily stored, simply prepared, and can be obtained in a wide variety of delicious forms. The freeze-dry process removes almost all of the water from the food and therefore most of its weight. It is reconstituted by allowing the proper amount of water to soak back into the dried food substance. Since an adequate supply of water can be obtained from the fuel cells in Apollo and Gemini, the weight of the water used in preparation is not charged against the food supply weight budget. On future spacecraft it can be expected that potable water will be recovered from condensate and liquid waste as previously discussed. Thus only the dry weight of the food is significant. A days ration of freeze-dried food weighs only 19 ounces. The average amount of water needed for reconstituting this amount of food would be about four pounds.

Space Suits

Astronauts wear space suits for two purposes. First, they serve as a protective measure against inadvertant loss of cabin pressure from such causes as a meteoroid puncture, failure of one of the closure seals, or the failure of the cabin atmosphere system. The other purpose of space suits is to allow the crew to leave the spacecraft while in space or on the surface of the moon.

A space suit designed solely as an emergency garment is different from the extra-vehicular suit in several respects. The suit designed just as a protective device need only provide sufficient mobility when inflated for the wearer to continue to operate the spacecraft controls. The Mercury suit is an example of this type. It was tailored and fitted to the shape of the astronaut in the seated position. While it provided sufficient mobility for the astronauts to scan their display panel and to reach all the necessary controls while inflated, it made no concession to major movement of the torso and legs. As a matter of fact, the astronauts could not walk fully erect in this suit even when unpressurized,

Both the Gemini and Apollo suits can be used outside of the spacecraft. During some of the Gemini flights, the astronauts depressurize the cabin and open the hatch. One of the astronauts leaves the spacecraft and floats in space connected only by a tether. By leaving the cabin, the astronaut is able to carry out special experiments during the mission which involve equipment stored in the large adaptor section attached to the rear of the Gemini spacecraft.

When a space suit is employed inside the spacecraft, it is connected by hoses to the environmental control system. The environmental control system continually discharges cool, purified air into the space suit. This is conducted to the ends

Fig. 5-2. Development model of the Apollo space suit. (NASA)

of the arms and legs by flexible ducts inside the suit, where it is released to the inside of the pressure garment. The cool oxygen then flows back over the body of the astronaut, picking up body heat by convection and by evaporation of perspiration. The oxygen then flows into the helmet where it may be breathed. Another hose returns the oxygen, together with water and expired carbon dioxide from the helmet, to the environmental control system. A fan in the environmental control system keeps the oxygen circulating through the suit. When a space suit is used outside of the spacecraft, a portable system replaces the function of the cabin environmental control system.

The Apollo space suit is designed to sustain the crew in space and on the surface of the moon. It has been specially designed to minimize the restriction of motion of the arms and legs. Since the moon's surface is extremely hot on the sunlit side, the Apollo space suit includes a multi-layer insulation outer garment to minimize the amount of heat entering the suit from this source and from the sun. This heat, together with the metabolic heat produced by the astronaut, must be removed from the suit by the portable life support system.

Measurements have shown that it requires a great deal more energy to do things in a space suit than in ordinary clothes. The simple task of walking becomes hard work in a space suit because the internal pressure makes the joints resist motion. The consequence of this is that the rate of energy used by the astronaut on the surface of the moon will be very high. With the heat of the sun and moon leaking into the space suit, and with the high metabolic rate of the astronaut, the cooling system in the Apollo space suit will have a much greater cooling load than previous space suits. The previous practice of circulating oxygen to cool the astronaut under the above circumstances would not be adequate. The trouble is that the density of oxygen at 3.5 psi is so low that a very high circulation rate would be required to carry away this much heat. The electric power to drive the circulation fan would be so great that the amount of time the astronaut could spend outside the spacecraft would be undesirably restricted by the weight of electric batteries.

The Apollo space suit is designed to use water to cool the astronaut when he is outside the space ship. The portable life support system, which he carries on his back, continually circulates cool water to the suit. There are a network of small plastic tubes sewn in the undergarment of the suit that conduct heat away from the skin by direct contact. The circulating water is cooled in the portable life support system. Heat is removed from the cooling water in a heat exchanger, which in turn is cooled by the evaporation of additional water carried for this purpose. The use of water cooling has a side benefit. It greatly reduces the amount of perspiration normally

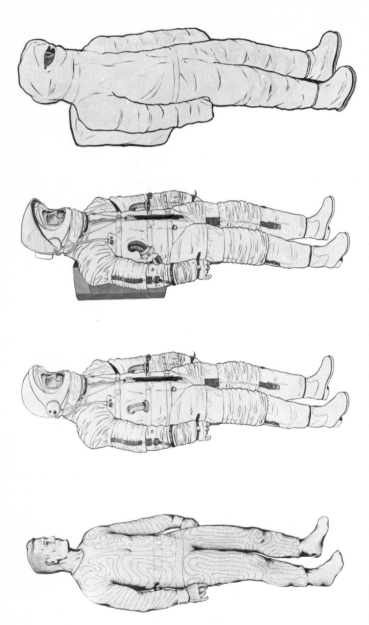

Fig. 5-3. Dress for lunar surface exploration: (left to right) water-cooled undergarment is worn next to skin, space suit proper, portable life support system is carried on back, and coveralls provide thermal insulation and protection from micrometeoroids. (NASA)

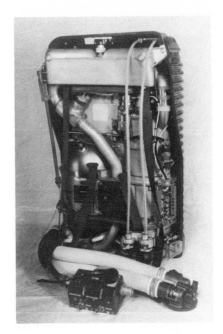

Fig. 5-4. The Apollo personal-life support system. (NASA)

experienced by those wearing space suits. This high perspiration rate in a gas-cooled suit is a result of the inadequacy of low density oxygen to cool by convection, and is the cause for the partial dehydration which sometimes occurs when space suits are worn for extended periods. It is estimated that 70 percent of the body's metabolic heat must be dissipated by perspiration in a gas-cooled space suit.

Acceleration

A space flight not only exposes the crew to the environment of weightlessness, but also to the stress of extended periods of high acceleration.

The gravitational force on Earth is part of the natural environment of all Earth's creatures. Therefore, it may be anticipated that a departure from this environment of "one g" for extended periods of time may cause physiological problems.

In discussing the physiological effects of acceleration, it is convenient to speak of g *loads*. The acceleration force divided by the weight at sea level is referred to as the number of g's that are being experienced. Similarly, the actual acceleration divided by the acceleration due to gravity at sea level is also equal to the g's being experienced.

$$g = F/W$$
or $\quad g = a/32.2$

where F = accelerating force in pounds, W = weight at sea level in pounds, and a = acceleration, ft/sec².

Although the crew experiences both acceleration and deceleration during a flight, it is common to refer to either situation simply as acceleration. The important consideration is the direction of the acceleration vector with respect to the torso of the crew. If the crew is facing forward and undergoing positive acceleration (speeding-up), then this is referred to as "eyeballs in" acceleration, since the effect of the acceleration load is to force the eyeballs backward into the head. Similarly, a pilot in an airplane that is doing a pull-up maneuver, would be experiencing an "eyeballs down" acceleration load. Other situations would be "eyeball right," "eyeball left," "eyeball out," and "eyeball up." This would then cover the six possible orthogonal directions. Naturally, there are combinations of these directions, along which the acceleration vector may be imposed. There are generally two types of acceleration loads that the spacecraft crew may experience. There is the long duration at moderate acceleration that is associated with powered flight and with atmospheric reentry, and there is the very short duration of high acceleration that may accompany landing impact or the jerk experienced if the ejection seat is used.

The apparent effect of acceleration is to make every part of the body weigh proportionately more than normal. Thus, when undergoing a 10 g acceleration, a 150 pound man would apparently weigh 1500 pounds. Each and every part of his body would apparently weigh ten times more than normally.

The physiological hazard of acceleration is associated with the distortion and stress to which the different parts of the body are subjected. Under extremely high acceleration loads, the body structure may be damaged. The bones may be fractured or dislocated, tendons may be injured, and organs may be torn loose or otherwise ruptured. The likelihood of occurrence of this type of damage is usually dependent upon the level of acceleration and the rapidity, or onset rate, by which it is imposed rather than the duration over which it persists. In other words, these types of injuries either will occur before or during the period that the peak acceleration is reached, or will not occur at all.

The onset rate of acceleration is a consideration that perhaps needs further explanation, since it is in itself an important contribution to injury. The reason is that the body responds like an elastic structure. In other words, parts of the body will sag and distort under the load of high acceleration. The effect is that these parts do not initially follow the basic motion and must catch up at a slightly later instant by accelerating at an even higher level. The resulting peak level of acceleration may cause an injury that otherwise would not occur. An example of this is the whiplash injury to the neck that often occurs in automobile collisions. Consequently, engineers attempt to design shock attenuation systems that do not create excessive onset rates. At the same time, the desire is to design the couch that supports the crew in a manner that the body will be held firmly to minimize sagging and distortion. Figure 5-5 is a diagram of acceleration that is considered to be safe for short duration, provided the onset rate does not exceed the indicated value. These tolerances are for a firmly supported individual.

Besides the danger of direct structural damage to the body as previously discussed, a protracted period of acceleration may cause physiological damage by interfering with blood circulation. This is because the blood will tend to settle to the lowest point in the body. Even at normal earth gravity condition, the blood in the body would tend to settle to the feet (while standing) if it were not for the fact that the veins in the lower portion of the body automatically contract sufficiently to maintain the desired distribution of blood. However,

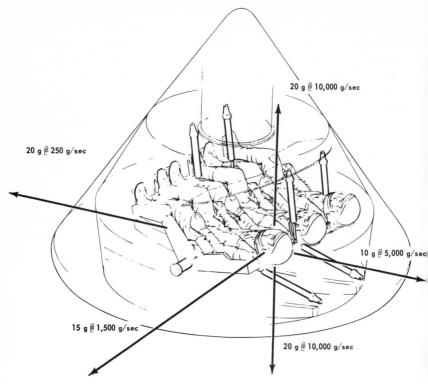

20 g @ 10,000 g/sec

20 g @ 250 g/sec

10 g @ 5,000 g/sec

15 g @ 1,500 g/sec

20 g @ 10,000 g/sec

Fig. 5-5.   The known safe human tolerances to impact. (NASA)

at a sufficiently high level of g, the circulation system can no longer compensate and the blood tends to pool at the lower regions. The "black-out" of fighter pilots in a sharp pull-up maneuver is an example. In this situation, the blood pools in the feet and circulation of freshly oxygenated blood to the brain is impaired. Since vision is sensitive to oxygen lack, the pilot becomes temporarily blind during this experience.

It has been found that a modified supine position (knees raised and head slightly higher than hips) is favorable for maintaining blood circulation even at moderately high acceleration. In this position, the heart is assured a generous supply of blood returning from the veins. Furthermore, the distance "uphill" to the head is not so great that the heart is unable to keep arterial blood flowing to the brain. It was in this position that the Mercury crews sustained a reentry deceleration that reached almost 8 g's. In centrifuge experiments a volunteer has successfully withstood simulated atmosphere reentries that exceeded 20 g's, remaining conscious throughout the time.

Weightlessness

Prior to the first space flight, there was much conjecture on the physiological effect of weightlessness. This was because earth-bound creatures could only experience this condition for very short periods of time. The longest periods of weightlessness that were experienced were produced in airplanes. To create weightlessness, the pilot of the airplane flies a carefully planned maneuver that starts with a high-speed pull-up. With the airplane flying in a steep climb at high speed, the pilot then flies along a parabolic path. He carefully controls the flight so that no aerodynamic lift or side forces are produced, and so that the engine thrust exactly overcomes the drag. This maneuver starts with the airplane going up and terminates with the airplane in a steep dive. With a high performance airplane, the state of weightlessness can be maintained for about 40 seconds.

Now that both American and Russian astronauts have experienced the condition of weightlessness for significant periods of time, the fear that man would not be able to adapt to this condition has largely disappeared. During these flights, the physiological tests made and the subjective experiences of the crew all indicate that there was little or no difficulty in adapting to the weightless condition. The consensus from the American crews was that the adjustment was easy and that the sensation was, if anything, pleasant. There is no indication in the physiological data of any functional difficulty. Other stresses of the flight—such as partial dehydration (associated with space suit ventilation)—could easily account for small abnormalities in the data.

There does seem to be some evidence of possible physical deconditioning of the type that is common during periods of bed confinement. This is the general loss of physical condition and the feeling of weakness that often follows a period of convalescence. During bed confinement, the muscles are not sufficiently exercised and the cardiovascular system is only required to work with the body horizontal. A consequence of the lack of exercise is that the muscles lose their tone and calcium from the bones goes into the blood and is subsequently lost to the body in urine. This mobilization of the bone calcium is a well-known phenomena and will start to occur within a day. It is probable that a daily regime of planned exercise will be needed in protracted space missions as a replacement for the physical effort needed for daily activity in Earth's gravitation environment.

The effects of extended periods in bed on the cardiovascular system is that the heart and veins become adapted to the horizontal position. In this position, the blood is not required to flow uphill in returning from the lower extremities and consequently the veins stay relaxed. Upon returning to an upright position after an extended period in bed, an individual will feel faint and may pass out. His veins have lost their "tone" and do not contract sufficiently to prevent blood from pooling in the legs. The consequence is that, although the pulse rate greatly increases, the heart is unable to maintain an adequate supply of blood to the brain. Both Cooper and Schirra experienced faintness at the termination of their flights when they first stood erect. However, such symptoms may also be attributed to the dehydration and fatigue that was caused by wearing a space suit throughout the duration of the mission. Thus, at the time of this writing, there is no evidence of any unfavorable effects of weightlessness during the flight. There appears to be some possibility of temporary post-flight effects associated with readjustment to Earth's gravity. If this turns out to be a serious problem, there are several preventatives under study that have proven to be effective when used in laboratory simulations, such as water emersion tests.

6

Tracking and Communications

Although a manned spacecraft is designed to carry out its mission independent of the support of the facilities on Earth, it is intended that this be done only as an emergency flight mode. Actually, extensive facilities have been constructed on Earth to provide every reasonable and practical aid to the flight. These ground facilities are manned by operations support teams which help the flight crew monitor the performances of all the vital systems aboard the spacecraft as well as assist them in flight navigation. In fact the facilities on the ground are able to provide more precise and more reliable navigation data than that which can be generated aboard the spacecraft. Thus, the communication and tracking links between spacecraft and ground are vital elements of a manned space mission.

Radar tracking of the spacecraft is used to determine the position and velocity of the spacecraft. The position of an object is obtained from a radar set by measuring the elevation and azimuth angles of the radar beam illuminating a target and by measuring the time increment that it takes for a signal to make the round trip from the radar antenna to the target and back. This last measurement gives the radial distance to the target. Velocity is measured by the Doppler effect. The returned signal is changed in frequency by an amount that is directly proportional to the radial component of the target's velocity. While the radial component of velocity is in itself of little value this measurement combined with other measurements can be used to make accurate computations of velocity and direction of motion.

The location of the radar set on the earth must be determined to at least the same degree of accuracy that is desired for tracking the spacecraft. In addition, the radar must be boresighted to an accurate reference so that the measured elevation and azimuth angles will be of sufficient accuracy. The scanning accuracy of the radar beam is also limited by the sharpness of focus of the beam. Thus, a highly directional antenna must be used for high accuracy tracking. A radar with such a very narrow beam cannot be depended upon to acquire (initially find) the spacecraft. For this reason it is sometimes necessary to employ a broader beam antenna system as an acquisition aid. Another scheme is to use computed information to direct the steering of the radar antenna along the predicted track of the spacecraft while the radar acquires the target.

Because it is desired to track spacecraft at great distances, they are usually equipped with radar transponders. A transponder is a device which receives a radar signal, amplifies it and retransmits it on a slightly different frequency. The amplification of the radar signal in the transponder greatly increases the effective range of the radar.

In addition to radar tracking, radio frequency transmissions between the ground and spacecraft are used to transmit a great deal of information during the mission. The most important communications are by voice. The spacecraft crew keeps personnel on the ground informed of the status and performance of the spacecraft by this means. At the same time, those on the ground are able to advise and consult with the flight crew on problems which may arise. They are able to give the crew important navigation instructions based upon the precise and reliable information generated by the ground facilities.

Radio transmissions are also used to transmit data directly to remote display consoles, recorders, or to computers for further processing, This is also a two-way transmission; however, the majority of operational data is transmitted from spacecraft instrumentation to the ground activity. Some of these measurements are displayed to the ground monitoring crews while others are fed into computers which generate computed performance of the spacecraft or predicted capabilities for future maneuvers. Similarly, valuable data generated by the ground facilities can be transmitted to the spacecraft for display to the crew or to be stored in the spacecraft computer for future use.

The Mercury System

The communications and tracking equipment used on the Mercury is illustrative of the various kinds of equipment carried. Figure 6-1 is a phantom view of the Mercury capsule with the location of these components shown. Since the Mercury was tracked by both Verlort (S-band) and SC-584 (C-band) radar sets, both C-band and S-band beacons were carried. Three flush-mounted antennas were used on each in order that signals could be received and retransmitted in any direction. The bicone antenna at the front end of the capsule was used to receive and transmit voice commands on both UHF and HF frequencies, to transmit signals from two telemeter transmitters and to receive command signals from the ground. A frequency multiplexer was carried to facilitate the use of all these channels of communication through one antenna. This antenna is formed by isolating the antenna fairing from the rest of the spacecraft by an insulating material (vicor). This was an omnidirectional antenna. Omnidirectional characteristics were desired since it was intended that the capsule be able to communicate with the network stations while it was in any attitude. The bicone antenna was jettisoned at 10,000 feet altitude when the main parachute was deployed. A spring loaded UHF antenna was deployed concurrently with this action to provide continuous communication for voice and telemetry. After landing, a quarter wave whip antenna was erected for HF recovery communication.

It can be seen that a great deal of redundancy in the communication system was employed in the Mercury project. This was done in order to insure continued communications in the event of one or more failures. Two types of radar beacons were employed because there was in existence both C-band and S-band radar sets at some of the sites that were chosen for part of the Mercury network. Two frequencies were used

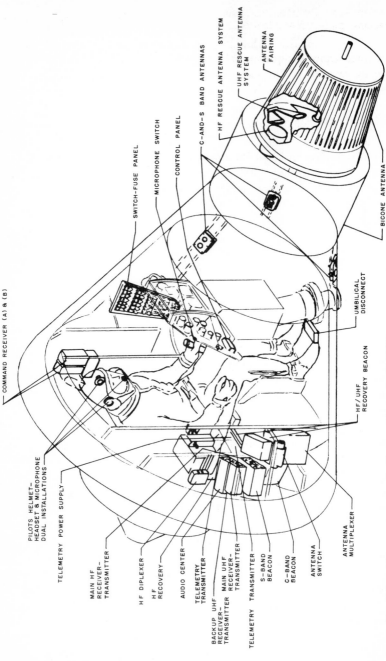

COMMAND RECEIVER (A) & (B)

PILOTS HELMET—
HEADSET & MICROPHONE
DUAL INSTALLATIONS

TELEMETRY POWER SUPPLY

MAIN HF
RECEIVER—
TRANSMITTER

HF DIPLEXER

HF
RECOVERY

AUDIO CENTER

TELEMETRY
TRANSMITTER

BACKUP UHF
RECEIVER—
TRANSMITTER

MAIN UHF
RECEIVER—
TRANSMITTER

TELEMETRY TRANSMITTER

S-BAND
BEACON

C-BAND
BEACON

ANTENNA
SWITCH

ANTENNA
MULTIPLEXER

SWITCH-FUSE PANEL

MICROPHONE SWITCH

CONTROL PANEL

C-AND-S BAND ANTENNAS

HF RESCUE ANTENNA SYSTEM

UHF RESCUE ANTENNA
SYSTEM

ANTENNA
FAIRING

BICONE ANTENNA

UMBILICAL
DISCONNECT

HF/UHF
RECOVERY BEACON

Fig. 6-1.   Mercury communication equipment. (NASA)

for voice transmission because it was not certain which frequency would be most useful during the mission. UHF frequencies seemed certain to be able to penetrate the upper reaches of the atmosphere. Although HF frequencies may sometimes be deflected by these layers, they are also able to travel beyond the horizon by skipping between the Earth's surface and the ionosphere. The command receiver was used to receive instructions from the ground which could initiate an abort or the firing of the retro-rockets. It was also able to reset the clock which was timed to automatically initiate the retro-rocket firing and to initiate calibration signals for the onboard instrumentation.

The two telemeter transmitters were arranged so that they operated in parallel. There were a total of over 90 separate things that were measured during the flight. Each of the quantities measured was transmitted over both telemeters for redundancy. A tape recorder was also carried which recorded all the same data and all the voice transmissions. This provided a complete record which could be used for postflight analysis of the spacecraft performance. The information measured included accomplishment of a great number of individual events, such as the deployment of the drogue parachute. Pressures, quantity of expendables, temperature, and acceleration were also measured. The functioning of certain systems such as the automatic control system, the environmental control system, and the power supply and conversion system were all monitored. The astronaut was also the subject of a number of measurements which included his heartbeat, his respiration, and his body temperature. Figure 6-2 shows the location of some of the Mercury spacecraft instrumentation.

One of the major efforts during the Mercury program was the establishment of a world-wide tracking and communications network. This network was designed to provide almost continuous communication with the spacecraft as it traveled around the world every 90 minutes. Initially, the network was designed to support missions of three orbits. In this case there were only a few periods when the spacecraft was not in line of sight of one of the network stations or ships for a period in

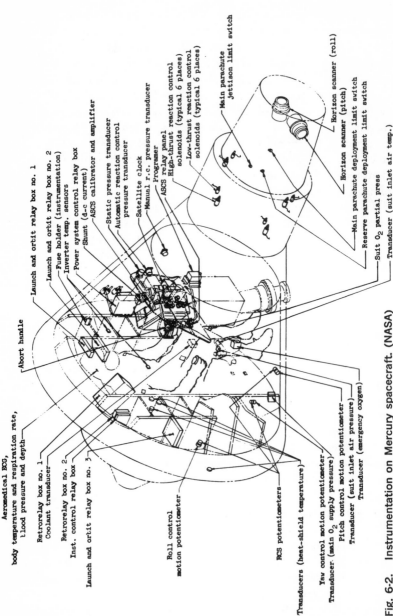

Fig. 6-2. Instrumentation on Mercury spacecraft. (NASA)

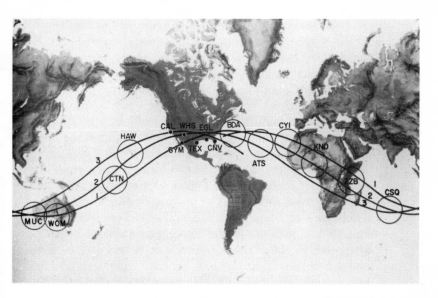

GROUND STATIONS FOR PROJECT MERCURY

		VOICE & TELEM.	S- OR C-BAND RADAR	COMMAND CAPABILITY
1.	ATLANTIC MISSILE RANGE	X	C	X
2.	BERMUDA	X	S-C	X
3.	MID-ATLANTIC SHIP	X	-	-
4.	CANARY ISLANDS	X	S	-
5.	KANO, NIGERIA	X	-	-
6.	ZANZIBAR	X	-	-
7.	INDIAN OCEAN SHIP	X	-	-
8.	MUCHEA, AUSTRALIA	X	S	X
9.	WOOMERA, AUSTRALIA	X	C	-
10.	CANTON ISLAND	X	-	-
11.	HAWAII	X	S-C	X
12.	SOUTHERN CALIFORNIA	X	S-C	X
13.	GUAYMAS, MEXICO	X	S	X
14.	WHITE SANDS	T	C	-
15.	CORPUS CHRISTI, TEXAS	X	S	-
16.	EGLIN (AFATC)	T	C	-

Fig. 6-3. Ground stations for Project Mercury. (NASA)

excess of ten minutes. Figure 6-3 is a map of the world show-
ing the world-wide network of stations and ships that provided
tracking and communication in support of the Mercury flight.

The various stations and ships in the network were tied into
the Mercury Control Center at Cape Kennedy, Florida. Land
lines, submarine cables and HF radio were used to provide the
communication links between the control center and the stations and ships. Both teletype and voice transmissions were
used to carry out the communication functions. The Mercury
Control Center and the network were also linked to the Computing and Communication Center at Greenbelt, Maryland.
This center was established to provide control, switching and
distribution of communications traffic and to perform the
requisite computations on the tracking data obtained from the
radars that would establish a precise orbit and determine the
proper time for firing the retro-rockets. Other computations
were required for decision-making purposes in the event that
a mission would have required an emergency termination.

Apollo Communication and Tracking

The Apollo mission creates a much more difficult tracking
and communications problem than did Mercury. This stems
not only from the fact that the Apollo spacecraft and mission
is much more complex, but also because great distances are
involved and multiple elements must be kept under surveillance. Figure 6-4 shows the many communication and tracking
tasks created by the fact that during certain mission phases,
the LEM is separated from the command module and a member of the LEM crew may be exploring the surface of the
moon. Mission operation procedures will require that these
separate elements must remain in contact with one another
and with the Manned Spacecraft Control Center, in order that
their activities are properly coordinated. This situation is of
course aggravated by the fact that a great deal of information
must be transmitted over very long distances. This results in a
requirement for highly directional antennas in order to avoid
high-power loads.

Fig. 6-4.   Communication links for Apollo mission.

One of the salient features of the Apollo system is the use of common equipment operating at S-band frequencies for both tracking and communications. Although this scheme complicates the modulation equipment, it achieves savings in the amount of transmitting and receiving equipment and antennas that must be carried in the spacecraft.

The signal transmitted from earth to the spacecraft consists of a 2100 MC carrier modulated by a coded subcarrier used for tracking and other subcarriers used for communications. The spacecraft has a transponder aboard that modifies the received carrier signal by increasing its frequency to 2300 MC. This new carrier signal is then returned to the Earth, modulated with the turned-around tracking signal, and with space-craft-to-ground communication subcarriers.

The tracking signal is a code sequence that is non-repetitive for a period of five seconds. Thus, when the returned signal is compared with the transmitted signal, the round trip time can be determined without ambiguity for times up to five seconds. This allows direct determination of the range between space-craft and the tracking station throughout the flight to the moon. The radial component of velocity between spacecraft and tracking station is determined by the Doppler shift in the tracking signal.

The tracking stations on earth will be able to communicate with both the command module and the lunar excursion module. This will be done by the use of slightly different carrier frequencies to allow for simultaneous communications. Both the lunar excursion module and the command module will receive voice communications and coded data from the ground. They will both also transmit voice and telemetry data to the ground and be able to transmit television to the ground during certain portions of the mission.

The command module and the lunar excursion module are also able to communicate between themselves. They do this with VHF equipment. The astronauts have personal communication sets in their space suit back-packs that are used for the short range communication to the lunar excursion module. This is also VHF equipment. It not only provides for two-way voice but also transmits biomedical measurements from the astronaut to the lunar excursion module, which in turn relays it to the earth.

The LEM and the command module both carry X-band radar sets to allow them to find and track each other during the rendezvous maneuver that takes place in lunar orbit after the lunar excursion module leaves the moon's surface. Each is also equipped with radar transponders to assist each other's rendezvous radar. The LEM also has a landing radar set. This radar will feed altitude and rate of descent measurements into the navigation computer. The information will then be employed in making an automatic controlled descent to the hover maneuver. During the landing maneuver, the altitude and rate of descent will be displayed to the pilot.

Apollo employs directional antennas in order to transmit all the requisite information over the S-band link without exorbitant power loads. Both the LEM and the service module will have steerable antennas. These will be automatically pointed to the Earth. The Earth will stand out as a warm area against the cold background of space; therefore, infrared sensors attached to the antenna will be used to generate steering signals which will keep the antenna aimed at the Earth.

By limiting the amount of information to be transmitted, the band width of a carrier signal can be greatly decreased. With a reduced band width, an acceptable signal can be transmitted at greatly reduced radiated power. Thus, a less efficient antenna that does not radiate as much power to the Earth will suffice if the band width is sufficiently reduced. Both the LEM and the service module carry omnidirectional S-band antennas. These antennas will allow degraded communications to continue between the spacecraft and tracking stations in the event that the steerable antennas malfunction. The omnidirectional antennas on the command module also provide for communication after the service module is jettisoned prior to atmosphere reentry. These antennas are flush-mounted on the conical portion to minimize the exposure to aerodynamic heating.

World-wide tracking and communication stations will be employed during both the short Earth orbital portion of the mission and the remainder of the mission period when Apollo is in cis-lunar space. This cis-lunar portion requires facilities capable of long range. At this time three stations properly located around the world are sufficient to keep the mission under constant surveillance. These stations will be equipped with antennas 85 feet in diameter. While in Earth orbit, the spacecraft will be in view of each of these stations for only a short period of time. Thus, additional stations with smaller antennas will be used to avoid extensive periods of communications blackouts during orbit, and to provide continuous communications during important maneuvers such as launch into orbit, departure from orbit, and reentry. All stations for the Apollo mission are tied into the Manned Spacecraft Control Center (MSCC), in Houston, Texas. At this location all mission communications traffic is classified and routed to pertinent activities. Besides its primary function of operations management and control, the MSCC also carries out all computations in support of the mission activities.

7

Electrical Power Generation in Space

There are a great many uses for electrical power on board a manned spacecraft. Power is used by the communications equipment, by the radar, navigation and guidance equipment, and by the automatic control system. The environment control system uses electricity to drive the blowers that circulate oxygen in the cabin and through the space suits of the crew, and then through purification and cooling equipment. Cooling fluids must be circulated past heat-producing equipment and then through external radiators. The cabin and the display panel are illuminated by electricity. In other words, virtually every piece of equipment aboard the spacecraft consumes some electrical power. Although each and every item is especially designed to use as little power as practical, there are so many power users that the total consumption is significant.

The power consumption rate on the Mercury spacecraft averaged about 500 watts. The Apollo command and service module will use power at perhaps four times this rate. By everyday standards these values may appear quite modest, but in a spacecraft, the production of electrical power is very costly from a weight standpoint.

There are two handicaps that a spacecraft must bear when it comes to production of power. In space, there is no air for the combustion of chemical fuels, and waste heat produced by the power generation is difficult to dispose of, since heat may only be rejected in space by radiation.

The type of system best suited to provide power in a spacecraft depends on a number of considerations. The primary considerations are the peak power rate required, the total amount of energy needed during the mission, and the total duration of the mission. All the above must include margins for contingencies that may be required to complete a mission under abnormal circumstances. Other considerations may rule out certain power generation systems, since the mode of operation of the particular system may unduly restrict the mission operation. In general, when the mission is short, the weight and complexity of the "dry" system is the primary consideration in selection. For long missions, on the other hand, the weight of consumables becomes the most important consideration.

Electrical energy can be produced aboard a spacecraft from either chemical, nuclear, or solar energy. Invariably, the conversion of energy from the raw source into usable electrical power involves processes that are not 100 percent efficient. This means that the amount of energy obtained in electricity is less than the amount of energy taken from the source. The difference between the useful energy output and the raw energy input is excess heat that cannot be used (in other words, waste heat). Since waste heat must be rejected from the spacecraft, the amount of waste heat produced in the power generation system may be a significant consideration in the selection and design of the system.

The simplest form of electric power supply is primary cells, more commonly called storage batteries. The energy source in primary cells is in the chemical properties of the cell materials. When the electricity is withdrawn from a battery which is a series of cells, a chemical reaction takes place within the individual cells. The chemical energy is converted into electricity as ions flow from the cathode to the anode in each cell. The energy that produces this current is obtained from chemical reactions taking place between the electrodes and the electrolyte in the cell.

Batteries are quite efficient in converting chemical energy to electrical energy. Very little waste heat is produced, and that which is produced can be easily disposed of by the regular spacecraft cooling system. Unfortunately, the best storage batteries do not store a great deal of available energy per pound of weight. The Mercury spacecraft used batteries to provide electric power. The standard unit was made up of a

battery of silver-zinc cells rated at 3000 watt hours. Since this
unit weighed 43 pounds, it produced only 70 watt hours per
pound of weight.

Primary cells are also used in Gemini and Apollo, as the
power supply for the reentry and recovery period. For the
majority of the mission time period, however, fuel cells will be
used to provide power for these spacecraft. The fuel cell is
different from the primary cells in that the chemical reactants
expended during the production of electricity in the fuel cell
can be continuously replenished. Therefore these chemicals
can be stored elsewhere. Thus, the total energy capacity of
this system is not limited by its physical capacity to contain
the reactants. Furthermore, the reactants chosen for spacecraft
application (hydrogen and oxygen) have a much greater
chemical energy per pound than those used in primary batteries. A valuable by-product of the hydrogen-oxygen fuel cell
is potable water which can be used by the crew for drinking
and food preparation.

While there are several types of hydrogen-oxygen fuel cells,
the type used in the Apollo service module will be described
in detail to illustrate how fuel cells operate. A basic cell is
shown schematically in Figure 7-1. It consists of a sandwich
of two sintered nickel electrodes separated by potassium
hydroxide electrolyte. Oxygen is fed through one of the sintered nickel electrodes to the electrolyte, while hydrogen is
fed through the other. At both electrodes, the sintered nickel
acts as a catalyst for the chemical reaction between electrolyte
and reactants. At the electrode at which oxygen is introduced,
the oxygen combines with water in the potassium hydroxide
to form the hydroxyl (OH^-) ion. This ion diffuses through the
potassium hydroxide until it comes in contact with the opposite electrode, where it combines with the hydrogen to form
water. Part of the water is discharged out of the cell through
the electrode (contra-flow of the hydrogen), the other part
remains in the cell to maintain a desired water balance in the
potassium hydroxide. This type of fuel cell can produce about
1200 watt hours per pound of reactant consumed, which is a
significant performance gain over the primary cell.

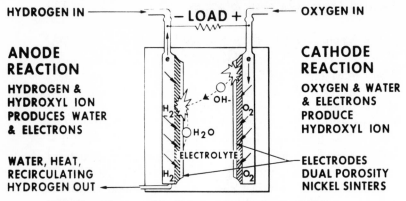

HYDROGEN IN ────── → ← - LOAD + ← ────── OXYGEN IN

ANODE REACTION

HYDROGEN & HYDROXYL ION PRODUCES WATER & ELECTRONS

WATER, HEAT, RECIRCULATING HYDROGEN OUT ◄──

CATHODE REACTION

OXYGEN & WATER & ELECTRONS PRODUCE HYDROXYL ION

ELECTRODES DUAL POROSITY NICKEL SINTERS

Fig. 7-1.   Diagram of hydrogen-oxygen fuel cell. (NASA)

Fig. 7-2.   Hydrogen-oxygen fuel cell. (NASA)

The Apollo fuel cell operates at the fairly high temperature of 425°F. The waste heat produced in the individual cells is more than sufficient to maintain this temperature. In fact, hydrogen is continually circulated between the cells and a cooling system to control the temperature in the cells. The water that is produced in the cells is carried out of the cells as steam by the circulating hydrogen, and is condensed in the heat exchanger of the cooling system. A water separator is used to remove the water from the circulating hydrogen. The arrangement for cooling and water removal is shown diagrammatically in Figure 7-3.

Primary cells were used as a power supply for the Mercury spacecraft which was designed for a one-day period in space. For Apollo and Gemini, which both have a nominal mission of two weeks, the hydrogen-oxygen fuel cell was determined to be the best source for electrical power. For missions of different durations, other systems will hold the competitive edge. For missions of a duration shorter than two weeks, but in excess of a few days, chemically fueled mechanical engines driving electric generators appear to be the optimum choice from a weight standpoint. Such engine-driven systems would develop only between a quarter to a half of the efficiency of a fuel cell, but would enjoy a lighter dry weight. These engines would operate in much the same manner as an earthbound gas turbine or internal combustion engine, with the exception that in addition to fuel, they must also be supplied with a chemical oxidizer to replace the normal air supply which is nonexistent in space.

For durations in excess of a few weeks, chemical power systems are not competitive with systems based on nuclear or solar energy. This is because solar energy systems require no fuel at all, and nuclear systems require only a very small amount of fuel. Solar energy systems suffer from the basic requirement that the energy collection system must be positioned so that it can receive energy from the sun. This not only imposes an extra duty upon the attitude control system, but also restricts the freedom to maneuver. On the other hand, nuclear energy systems may require heavy shielding to protect

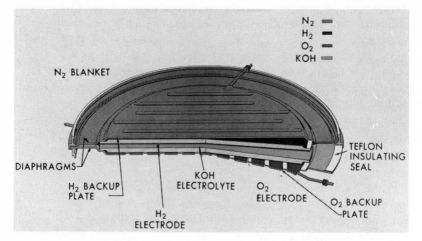

Fig. 7-3. Construction of flat electrode cell. Thirty-one cells of this type are used in the Apollo fuel-cell assembly. (NASA)

the crew from harmful radiation. Nevertheless, technology has advanced to the point where it is practical to build systems that could supply electrical power to manned spacecraft for periods in excess of one year using either solar or nuclear energy. Manned space laboratories and interplanetary spacecraft will undoubtedly be equipped with power systems using one or the other of these energy sources.

The most straightforward way to use solar energy is by photovoltaic conversion using solid state devices (solar cells). Such solar cells need only be exposed to sunlight to produce electrical energy. While only a small portion (perhaps six percent) of the solar energy falling on a cell may be converted into electrical energy, the simplicity and lightness of the solar cell, as well as the abundance of solar energy in space, make this an attractive way to provide power aboard a spacecraft. Waste heat is not a problem since each cell is able to act as its own radiator.

To supply adequate power for a large spacecraft will require thousands upon thousands of individual cells. This great number of cells will allow the use of circuit arrangements that should continue to provide adequate power in spite of the failure of individual cells or groups of cells during the lifetime of the spacecraft.

Solar energy can also be concentrated by a parabolic mirror and focused as a heat source. The thermal energy thus obtained may then be converted to electricity by one of numerous methods.

The most practical way to use nuclear energy to produce electricity is to first convert the nuclear energy into thermal energy. Heat can be generated by a nuclear reactor or by the use of the energy created by the decay of short half-life radioisotopes. Nuclear reactors suffer from the handicap of requiring very heavy shielding. If there is a need for a large quantity of power, as might be the case if electric propulsion is employed, then nuclear reactors may be the most practical means for power production.

In comparison to a nuclear reactor, there are several attractive features found in the use of radioisotope fuel. Radioisotopes release energy at a steady but slowly decreasing rate without any need for control, and without the danger of a runaway reaction. Power generation systems using isotopes that decay with alpha emissions require little or no special shielding, since alpha particles have very little penetration capability. Another advantage is that there is no special restriction on the size of the power-generating unit that can be constructed. The heat output and therefore the power level is dependent upon the activity level of the particular radioisotope employed, and the mass of the radioisotope constituent in the fuel charges. Thus, small, lightweight, compact power generation systems are feasible using radioisotope fuel. The main problems associated with the use of radioisotope fuel are associated with the fact that the fuel charge cannot be "turned off." It starts producing heat from the moment it is manufactured. This means that it should be manufactured only a short time before it is to be used, otherwise it will deplete itself as the quantity of radioisotope mass remaining becomes reduced through radioactive decay. And of equal importance is the fact that from the time the fuel charge is manufactured, it relentlessly releases heat that must be removed. This not only complicates storage, but also is very bothersome once it becomes installed in the spacecraft, which may be a significant time before launch.

Both the nuclear reactor and the radioisotope fuel charge are heat producers. To convert the thermal energy produced, these heat sources must be used in conjunction with a heat sink. A heat sink is a cold region providing a means for dumping waste heat from the energy conversion process. In space, the only practical heat sink is a thermal radiator.

One way to convert thermal energy into useful power is with a heat engine. There are numerous schemes for doing this. A simple scheme is with a steam turbine as shown in Figure 7-4. High pressure steam is generated by pumping liquid at high pressure through the heat exchanger of the heat source. The high pressure steam drives the turbine. The low pressure exhaust from the turbine is then condensed into water in the heat exchanger of the radiator (heat sink). This water is then fed to the pump and repeats the cycle. Other

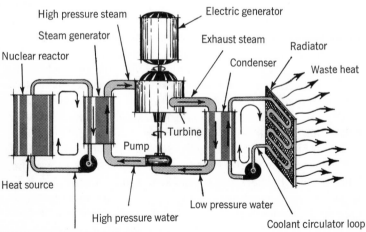

Fig. 7-4. Electric power generation from nuclear energy.

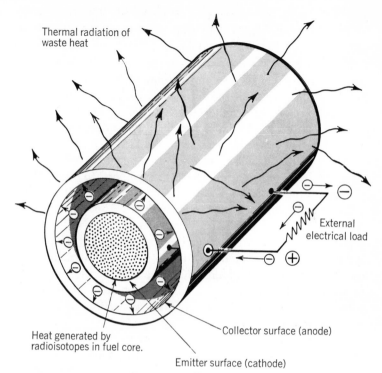

Thermal radiation of waste heat

External electrical load

Heat generated by radioisotopes in fuel core.

Collector surface (anode)

Emitter surface (cathode)

Fig. 7-5. Cross section of a thermionic generator powered by radio-isotope fuel.

working fluids such as mercury may be superior to water for power generation in space.

The size of the radiator is a compromise between weight and efficiency. A large radiator area will minimize the equilibrium temperature at which the heat can be dumped and thereby maximize the thermodynamic efficiency. On the other hand, a small radiator operating at a higher temperature would minimize the weight.

There are a number of techniques for static (no moving parts) conversion of thermal energy into electricity. One of the more promising schemes is with a thermionic converter. A thermionic converter works in a manner similar to a gas-filled diode. It employs a stream of electrons flowing, from a hot emitter (cathode) to a cold collector (anode), to create an electric current in the external circuit.

Figure 7-5 schematically shows a thermionic converter using a radioisotope fuel core as a heat source. The fuel is encapsulated by the emitter of the thermionic converter. The emitter is thereby raised to a sufficiently high temperature that some of the electrons in the emitter material are sufficiently excited to be expelled from the emitter at a sufficiently high velocity to travel to the collector, which is at a negative voltage with respect to the emitter. The collector is arranged to radiate heat to space. This keeps it cool so that the emission electrons that strike it will stick and not be re-emitted. This action is encouraged by filling the space between emitter and collector by certain low pressure gases such as cesium vapor. The vapor suppresses the formation of an electron cloud which would repel the movement of emission electrons across the space between electrodes. The thin film of cesium molecules that cling to the collector also assist in the deposition of emission electrons to this surface.

Thermionic converters also appear attractive for spacecraft power systems when used with other heat sources such as a nuclear reactor or a solar heat source. Another device for the direct conversion of thermal energy to electricity is the thermoelectric converter. This device employs the selective motion of charges in semiconductor material to convert a thermal potential into electricity. It can be seen that, with a variety of both thermal energy sources and conversion methods to choose from, suitable electrical power systems can be developed for future spacecraft regardless of size or mission.

8

Return to Earth

At the termination of its space mission, a manned spacecraft is expected to return the crew safely to the surface of the earth. By the very nature of space flight, however, a spacecraft can be expected to be traveling at speeds equal to or greater than orbital velocity when it starts its descent to the Earth's surface. With velocities of this magnitude, the spacecraft possesses a huge amount of kinetic energy. Since it is traveling at a great distance above the earth's surface, it also possesses a considerable amount of potential energy. This energy must all be safely dissipated before the spacecraft comes to rest. This is done during the atmospheric reentry and the subsequent landing maneuver.

The spacecraft is exposed to severe aerodynamic heating during the reentry maneuver. Thus, atmospheric reentry might be regarded as a bothersome hazard as far as space flight operations are concerned. Nothing could be further from the truth. If the atmosphere did not exist in a form suitable for decelerating spacecraft from their operating velocities, then return from space would require rocket propulsion for deceleration. The weight penalty for this would be enormous. An orbital flight, for instance would not only require sufficient propulsion to lift and accelerate the spacecraft to orbital conditions, but also to decelerate and lower the spacecraft to the surface of the earth. This would mean that the propulsion system would be required to produce twice the total velocity increment that is required just for attaining orbit. Since the weight of a propulsion system is an exponential function of the velocity it can impart to a payload, the weight at launch would be many times greater.

A typical orbital payload is about three percent of the

weight of the launch vehicle. If the payload reaching orbit were to include the propulsion to return a spacecraft to the surface of the earth by propulsive means alone, then such a spacecraft would be only three percent of the orbital payload. This would mean that the weight of the spacecraft would be only .09 percent of the launch weight. Thus, we are indeed fortunate that the atmosphere easily accommodates the deceleration of the spacecraft at the cost of a relatively small additional weight for heat protection.

The characteristic of the atmosphere which makes it ideal for deceleration is the way its density varies with altitude. At sufficiently high altitudes the atmosphere is thin enough to offer no significant drag. However, the density of the atmosphere doubles every three to five miles of altitude decrease. Therefore, the density gradually increases as the spacecraft descends through the atmosphere.

Let us imagine a ballistic (non-lifting) spacecraft returning along a path that carries it down into the atmosphere. Since its drag is primarily dependent upon atmospheric density, it can be seen that its rate of deceleration will tend to increase in the same manner that the density of the atmosphere increases. That is, its deceleration will double in magnitude again and again every time a certain time increment is passed. The time needed for each doubling of the deceleration is the time required to descend through a doubling of the atmospheric density. If the spacecraft is descending at a shallow angle, then it may take as much as a minute for the initial deceleration rate to double. However, if it is entering along a steep path, as in the case of a ballistic missile warhead, it may double in a matter of seconds.

The rate of deceleration does not continue to double and redouble indefinitely. This is because drag is a function of velocity as well as density. When the spacecraft first encounters the atmosphere, the rate of deceleration is very low and consequently very little velocity is lost (in other words, the velocity remains almost constant). However, since the deceleration is increasing exponentially, it is obvious that in time a significant lowering of the drag will be brought about through the loss of velocity. Eventually, the rate of loss in velocity becomes so great that the drag will decrease, although the density continues to increase. The result is that a peak deceleration is reached and then the rate of deceleration subsides.

The above description of a ballistic reentry is simplified in that it does not account for a number of other significant effects. For instance, since the world is round, the spacecraft can only maintain a constant rate of descent if its flight path has a radius of curvature equal to its distance from the earth's center. To do this it must be traveling at the velocity of a circular orbit. If it is traveling faster than this velocity, its rate of descent will gradually decrease; if it is traveling at less than circular velocity, it will curve downward and its rate of descent will be increasing.

Naturally, as it starts encountering atmospheric drag, its velocity will decrease and (presuming it started at orbital velocity) it will immediately start curving downward at a higher rate of descent. Thus, the rate at which the deceleration increases will increase as the flight path steepens. The effect of this is that a peak deceleration in excess of 7 g's will be encountered during an orbital return, regardless of how shallow an angle is chosen for the initial encounter with the atmosphere.

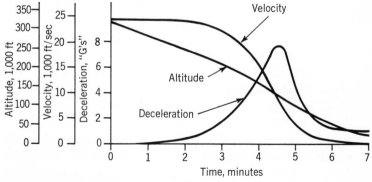

Fig. 8-1.   Reentry history for a typical Mercury mission.

Aerodynamic Considerations

For some time, there has been a great controversy among spacecraft designers concerning the aerodynamic configuration (shape) of manned spacecraft. This controversy is centered about the amount of aerodynamic lift required during reentry and landing the spacecraft. The debate over the need for lift started prior to the beginning of the Mercury project and will no doubt continue for many more years. Before proceeding further, the reader should be informed that the author has definite opinions on this subject and does not pretend to disguise them. For instance, *a very low value of lift-to-drag ratio provides the optimum spacecraft design.* It is hoped, however, that the following discussion may show the fundamental aerodynamic considerations associated with the reentry flight of manned spacecraft.

The external shape or configuration of the spacecraft during reentry determines its aerodynamic characteristics. Therefore, it is by developing better or different shapes that the aerodynamacist is able to produce those aerodynamic characteristics which suit the needs of succeeding generations of spacecraft. Typically, the spacecraft configuration should be aerodynamically stable, have low aerodynamic heating and provide the desired value of lift-to-drag ratio.

One of the chief differences in subsonic aerodynamics and hypersonic aerodynamics is the relative effectiveness of solid bodies and two-dimensional surfaces for producing forces normal to the flow direction. At speeds below the speed of sound, a streamlined body (such as the fuselage of an airplane) when yawed to the wind will produce a very small amount of side force relative to that produced on wing or tail surfaces. Therefore, sufficient tail surface area to stabilize such a body is small. The effectiveness of aerodynamic surfaces remains high throughout the subsonic and transonic speed ranges. However, as speed is increased significantly above the speed of sound, the effectiveness of such a surface to produce lift diminishes. This loss in effectiveness is particularly true at small angles-of-attack where the lift effectiveness is approximately inversely proportional to the Mach number. Thus, the effectiveness of a fin at Mach 10 would be only a fifth of its effectiveness at Mach 2. Compounding this problem is the fact that the effectiveness of bodies changes in an opposite fashion. That is, they are more effective at supersonic speeds in producing side force or lift when yawed or pitched.

This loss in effectiveness of fins with increased Mach number is limited to very small angles-of-attack. As the angle-of-attack is increased, the loss in effectiveness becomes much less pronounced, and at very high angles of attack (above 30°), there is very little change in lift effectiveness with change in Mach number.

Since conventional aerodynamic surfaces suffer such a large loss in effectiveness, other ways have been sought to stabilize missiles and spacecraft at hypersonic velocities. There have been several approaches used. First, the fins may be given a wedge-shaped cross section, instead of a conventional airfoil shape. This is shown in Figure 8-2. With such a cross section, the two surfaces of the fin are at a significant angle-of-attack even when the fin itself is at zero angle-of-attack. The greater the angle between the surfaces, the greater will be the effectiveness of such a fin at high speeds. The penalty for this, of course, is the increased drag that is produced by the forward-facing surfaces of the wedge and blunt trailing edge. Examples of vehicles that employ wedge fins are the X-15 and the Little Joe. Although the X-15 uses a wedge airfoil to increase the effectiveness of the vertical fin, the required fin area

(a) Wedge airfoil   (b) Conventional airfoil

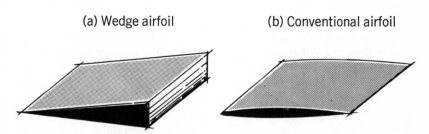

Fig. 8-2.   Wedge airfoil and conventional airfoil.

Fig. 8-3. The X-15 rocket plane. Note the wedge airfoil used on the vertical fin. (NASA)

is still very large. This clearly illustrates the great difficulty associated with stabilizing conventional streamlined bodies at hypersonic speeds.

Another scheme for providing stability at hypersonic speeds is to modify the body so that the rear portion will be an effective lift or side force producer. This is done by flaring the rear of the body. Such a body is said to have a flared tail. The flared tail may be thought of as a wedge airfoil that has been wrapped about the rear of the body. It has a distinct advantage over the fin-stabilized body in that it has no leading edge. Leading edges are extremely vulnerable to aerodynamic heating and are likely to become a major design problem at the same speeds that fins begin to have doubtful effectiveness for stabilization. Thus, the flared tail not only provides stability but avoids a nasty heating problem.

There is another approach to achieving stability that is most important for spacecraft configuration. In this case, the basic body shape itself is made to be aerodynamically stable. This is achieved when the center of pressure of the body configuration is behind its center of mass. Because spacecraft are usually made very compact, all the internal volume should be utilized. Although some of the heavy equipment can be located well forward in the spacecraft, the center of mass is usually not far from the center of volume. Thus, practical spacecraft configuration should have the aerodynamic center of pressure close to or behind the center of volume.

A cone and a sphere are examples of bodies that can easily be made stable. The aerodynamic pressure on the surface of a yawed cone is constant along any ray extending from the apex to the base. The pressure on the windward side will be greater than the pressure on the leeward side. But because the pressure is constant along the rays, the exact distribution of pressure around the cone is not significant in the determination of the cone's center of pressure. This is because the cone's surface can be analyzed by dividing it longitudinally into a great number of very slender triangles, each of which will have a constant surface pressure. Since the center of area of each triangle is the same distance back from the apex of the cone, the cone's center of pressure must be at the locus of the perpendiculars extended from the centers of these triangles.

Figure 8-5 shows the location of the center of pressure for two different cones. It should be noted that the more slender cone has its center of pressure further forward than the

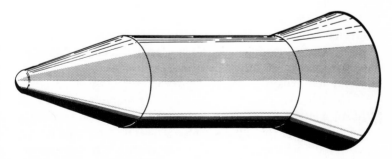

Fig. 8-4.   Body with flared tail.

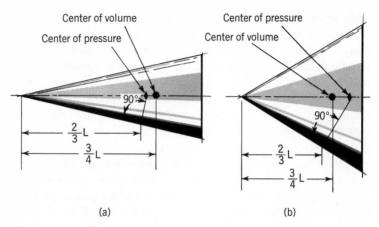

Fig. 8-5. (a) The center of pressure is ahead of the center of volume in this slender cone; (b) in this blunt cone, the center of pressure is behind the center of volume.

blunter one. The center of volume for all cones is three-quarters of the distance from the apex to the base. In the example, the slender cone would have its center of pressure ahead of the center of volume, whereas the center of pressure for the blunt cone is behind the center of volume. Thus, it can be seen that it would be easy to utilize the volume in the blunt cone without having the center of mass behind the center of pressure.

The explanation for the stability of a cone is exact only in cases where the flow over the surface of the cone is supersonic. However, the location of the center of pressure is not greatly affected when the velocity is reduced to below the speed of sound. A great many configurations for spacecraft and missiles are essentially derivations from a conical shape.

The aerodynamic center of pressure for a sphere is at its center. This is because a sphere is a unique shape. A line drawn perpendicular from any point on the surface of a sphere will pass through its center. Thus all aerodynamic pressure forces on the surface of a sphere will also be directed either toward or away from its center. Therefore, regardless of

what the aerodynamic pressure distribution is, the net effect
will always be a force acting through the sphere's center. To
make a sphere aerodynamically stable, one must merely locate
the center of mass toward the end of the sphere which is to be
the front.

At speeds greatly in excess of the speed of sound, only those
surfaces which face forward are subjected to significant aerodynamic pressure. That portion of the body which is behind
its largest cross section is in the wake of the body. At very
high speeds, the wake region is at such a low pressure that
minor variations in the pressure in this area are unimportant
compared to the forebody pressure. Thus the shape of the
forebody and the distribution of aerodynamic pressure over
its surface dictate the aerodynamic forces and moments experienced by the spacecraft during reentry flight. The Mercury, Gemini, and Apollo spacecraft are all designed with
blunt forebodies of spherical curvature. The center of pressure of each is near the center of curvature of the forebody.

For symmetrically shaped spacecraft such as have been discussed, only drag forces are encountered when the spacecraft
is precisely aligned so that its axis of symmetry lies on the
flight path. If the spacecraft is made assymmetrical, or if it is
trimmed by displacing the center of mass above or below the
axis of symmetry, then "lifting" as well as drag forces may be
generated.

With the Mercury spacecraft, great care was exercised to
locate the center of mass close to the center line. Mercury
therefore produced only incidental lift forces during reentry.
Since the landing point prediction was based on the assump-
tion that Mercury's flight path would not be deviated by even
small lift forces, Mercury was made to roll continuously during its reentry. This served to nullify minor errors in trim.

In the case of Apollo and Gemini, it is intended to maintain
active control of the landing point during reentry. Consequently a modest lifting force is desired. Both of these spacecraft are built with the center of mass below the center line of
the spacecraft. Consequently, these spacecraft are stable during reentry with an angle-of-attack of about 20°.

Trimmed at such an angle-of-attack, these spacecraft will generate a lift force equal to about one-third of the drag force. By controlling the roll orientation of the spacecraft, the guidance computer is able to control the reentry flight path. When the capsule is upright, the reentry range will be increased by the lift. When upside down, the range will be shortened. Banking to left will deviate the path to the left and so forth. When the flight path needs no correction, the capsule is set into a constant rotation.

Figure 8-6 diagrammatically illustrates the way in which a lifting force is generated on these spacecraft. Figure 8-6(a) shows the trimmed flight attitude when the spacecraft has its center of mass located on its center line. In Figure 8-6(b), the center of mass is displaced downward and a new trimmed flight attitude is shown. The heavy arrow that passes through both the center of gravity and center of pressure (this is the condition that establishes the trimmed attitude) is the aerodynamic force vector. This force vector implies the direction and location of the sum of all aerodynamic forces. In Figure

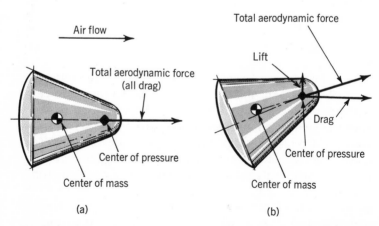

Fig. 8-6. Effect of displacement of center of mass upon trimmed attitude and lift; (a) center of mass on center line, trimmed for zero lift; (b) center of mass above center line, trimmed for lift/drag $\simeq 1/3$.

Fig. 8-7.   Lifting body derived from a cone.

8-6(a), it can be seen that the aerodynamic force vector is pointing directly backward. This means that only drag forces are being generated. In Figure 8-6(b), the aerodynamic force vector is pointing upward as well as backward. This force can be separated into a drag and lift force as shown by the drag and lift vectors in Figure 8-6(b).

It can be seen that although the spacecraft is trimmed "nose-down," the lift vector is upward. This is the exact opposite to the lift characteristic of conventional aircraft. The "negative lift" is a characteristic peculiar to very blunt bodies.

Conical-shaped bodies also can be made to produce lift by trimming them to fly nose-up. However, it is awkward to do this by displacement of the center of mass as in the case of the blunt bodies. It has been found that by modifications of the shape of the cone, desirable lift characteristics can be created.

A simple modification is to slice a cone in two along its center line and thereby produce a half-cone. Such a shape is shown in Figure 8-7. A shape of this type will naturally produce lift when trimmed so that axis of the original cone is parallel to the direction of flight. Since this can be achieved with a convenient center of mass location, this shape is a practical spacecraft configuration. There is one further minor modification necessary. The tip of the cone must be rounded off in order to avoid the excessive heating that would otherwise exist at this point. With configurations of this type, it is quite easy to achieve a lift value equal or greater than the value of the

Fig. 8-8. HL-10 configuration. This reentry body was specially de-signed to provide good, low-speed aerodynamic performance. (NASA)

drag. However, this type of configuration has a lower value of drag than the blunt bodies used on current spacecraft and therefore suffers from a greater aerodynamic heating load.

Further modifications of the half-cone shape have resulted in configurations of the type shown in Figure 8-8. Configurations of this type have been created by NASA research laboratories to have desirable low-speed aerodynamic characteristics. The flying qualities of these configurations at low speeds appear to be superior to those of the X-15 research aircraft. Thus, it can be said that these configurations are really "flying bodies" that can be glided to the surface of the earth for a conventional dead-stick landing at a suitable location.

Airflow Over a Blunt Body

It is desirable to transfer as much of the energy of the re-entering body into the air through which it passes. This is done by selecting reentry shapes which maximize the wave drag and minimize aerodynamic heating. Some aspects of air-

flow over bodies will be discussed in order to explain aerodynamic drag and heating. In order to keep the explanations
brief, certain oversimplifications will be used. To begin with,
it is conventional to consider that the air is moving and the
body is still, although, except for special cases such as wind
tunnel tests, the opposite is true.

Figure 8-9 is a shadowgraph of the airflow passing over the
Mercury capsule at hypersonic velocity. There is a very strong
shock wave standing some distance in front of the capsule.
The stand-off distance is great enough to allow the air that
passes through the shock wave to flow around the blunt face
to the shoulder. At locations outward from the center, the
shock wave bends back. The further outward, the greater is
the angle that the shock wave is bent. The strength of the
shock wave is greatest when it is normal to the flow and
diminishes as the angle changes from this. If the shock wave

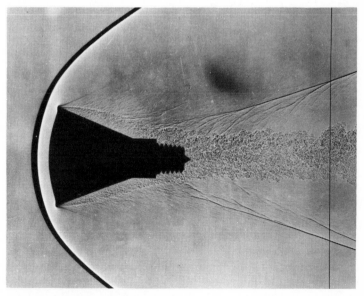

Fig. 8-9.   Schlieren photograph of Mercury model illustrating airflow
at hypersonic velocity. (NASA)

were to be examined at a sufficiently great distance outward from the body, it would become parallel to the Mach angle and would have no significant strength at this location.

The air that passes through the shock wave near its center suffers a great increase in entropy. When this air finally returns to a direction nearly parallel to its initial flow direction, some distance behind the capsule, it will have suffered a significant loss in velocity and have gained some temperature. This is because of the gain in entropy it experienced in passing through the shock wave. Air passing through other regions of the shock wave undergoes the same phenomena to a degree that is determined by the strength of the shock wave.

The significance of the changes in velocity and temperature is that this is indicative of the amount of work that the body performs on the air as it passes through it. This work manifests itself as air drag deceleration. Thus, there is an exchange of kinetic energy from the reentering body into thermal energy in the air. Simultaneously, the momentum of the reentering body is transferred into the air that it drags along behind it. Thus, this shock wave is the major mechanism creating drag for bodies of this type.

Another much weaker drag source is a second shock wave that is generated in the wake of the body. Still another source of drag is the boundary layer. Air in the boundary layer loses velocity through viscous friction to the surface of the body. Boundary layer action is intimately associated with aerodynamic heating and will be discussed later. In summary, a body traveling through the air at supersonic velocities generates a bow shock wave. This shock wave compresses the air with some loss in thermodynamic efficiency. Consequently, where the air re-expands, it cannot return to its initial conditions. The net result is that a large mass of air surrounding the path is slightly heated and is dragged along at a small velocity in the direction of flight. These effects account for the exchange in energy and momentum, respectively, associated with the drag of the reentering body. The blunter the body, the stronger will be the shock wave and the greater will be the drag.

Aerodynamic Heating

Aerodynamic heating is a phenomena which occurs in high speed flight. It is a result of two things. First, at very high velocities, air will become very hot when its kinetic energy is transformed into heat. Second, this hot air will transfer some of its heat to the body by convection as it passes over it. The *boundary layer* is a very thin layer just outside the surface of the body in which viscous effects are manifested. The boundary layer provides a mechanism for both decelerating the air flow (and thereby heating it) and for transferring heat from the air to the body. Thus, boundary layer phenomena is intimately associated with aerodynamic heating.

The molecules in air are in continual motion. They move at high velocity and in all directions, bouncing off each other as they frequently collide. Both the direction and velocity of travel of any given molecule is random, and change every time it collides with another molecule. The temperature of the air is a measure of the average energy of motion possessed by the molecules. The greater the energy of motion, the more rapidly the molecules move about and the higher is the air temperature. Thus, when air is heated, the molecules become more energetic and bounce about more. It is for this reason that the pressure increases proportionately with the temperature when a fixed quantity of air is heated in a constant volume container.

At low temperatures, all of the thermal energy in the air is contained in the random motion of the molecules. As higher temperatures are reached, the air molecules absorb some of the thermal energy in other ways. For instance, individual parts of the molecules may become excited and thereby store energy.

The individual molecules of air in motion not only contain random velocity but also the wind velocity. Only the velocity of random motion is measured as air temperature. However, if a stream of air is brought to a standstill, the additional velocity component that each molecule possessed (as part of the stream of moving air) is not lost, but manifests itself in an increase in the average random velocity. Thus, when moving air is brought to a standstill, its temperature rises. The temperature of moving air is therefore somewhat difficult to measure, since a thermometer will cause the air it contacts to come to a stop and become warm. However, this effect is negligible for the everyday winds which are encountered on the Earth's surface.

A reentering spacecraft moves through the air at many times the speed of the random motion of the air molecules. Thus in this case, a significant temperature increase can be brought about when the velocity of forward motion is added to the random velocity of the air molecules. The term *stagnation temperature* is used to describe the temperature that will result when the random velocity of the molecules is increased by the forward velocity. The term *static temperature* is used to describe the initial (or ambient) temperature of air prior to any velocity exchange. The following equation relates the stagnation temperature to the velocity.

$$T_S/T_O = 1 + .2\text{M}^2$$

where T_S = Stagnation temperature, T_O = Static temperature, and M = Mach number.

It can be seen that the stagnation temperature is extremely high for the case of a reentering spacecraft (up to M = 35 for lunar return). Actually, the equation does not hold true for such high temperatures. As previously explained, when sufficiently heated the air molecules can absorb energy by several modes of excitation. Furthermore, at these extremely high temperatures, the excitation may get sufficiently energetic to break the molecule itself into its atomic components. Atoms in turn may lose their outer ring electrons. However, these actions merely store energy which will remain and must be absorbed if the air is to be subsequently cooled from this condition.

In summary, when air impacts on a reentering spacecraft, or the shock wave that is created, the kinetic energy of the air (associated with the relative velocity between it and the spacecraft) is converted into thermal energy, which greatly increases the temperature of the air, and this may even cause the disassociation of some molecules and produce free electrons.

Intimately related to the action of the boundary layer is the viscosity of the air. Viscosity is that property of a fluid that resists a shearing motion. A good example of a very viscous fluid is honey. The reason that honey is more difficult to pour than water is that it resists moving over the surface of the jar. All fluids, including air, have some viscosity. Thus, motion of an object through air is resisted by the viscosity of the air. This viscous resistance takes place in a layer very close to the surface of the body called the boundary layer. Outside of the boundary layer, the air moves past the body in an essentially unimpeded manner. On the inside of the boundary layer, (right next to the surface of the body) the air is not moving at all relative to the body. In between these extremes, various layers of air move at intermediate velocities.

There are two types of boundary layers. These are termed *laminar* and *turbulent*. In a laminar boundary layer, the motion is very well-behaved. There is a smooth and continuous increase of velocity from the surface outward, and the character of the flow remains unchanged from one moment to the next. In the case of the turbulent flow, the boundary layer is highly disorganized. Although the average velocity measured over a period of time may vary smoothly with distance outward from the surface, the flow is continually changing in erratic surges throughout the boundary layer region.

Many of the details of boundary layer action are complicated; the overall effect, however, is fairly simple. The boundary layer is simply the region wherein the air moving in the free stream (and its energy and momentum) gets transported to the very thin layer just adjacent to the surface where it becomes completely degenerated into random motion of individual molecules. The transportation of the momentum of the outer layer to the surface creates a shear force on the surface and a drag on the spacecraft. This is called *skin friction drag*. The transportation of energy produces heat which may be conducted into the skin of the spacecraft. This is called *aero-dynamic heating*. Thus, the important thing about the boundary layer is that it provides the means for skin friction drag and aerodynamic heating. In a given flight situation, the severity of friction drag and aerodynamic heating are in proportion to each other. The things that tend to reduce skin friction drag also tend to reduce aerodynamic heating in the same proportion.

A blunt body is preceded by a very strong shock wave, whereas a pointed body will be preceded by a conical wave, considerably weaker. The strength of the shock wave, however, has no direct effect on the temperature of the air that eventually comes in contact with the skin. The reason for this may be clear if one considers the history of each individual air molecule that becomes involved. Prior to meeting the spacecraft, all air molecules are in motion with a modest random velocity that is associated with the ambient temperature of the air. When the air molecules encounter the strong shock wave of a blunt spacecraft, nearly the total velocity of the spacecraft is added to the random velocity of the air molecules. Thus, their new random velocity becomes very high and the air is extremely hot. The spacecraft is therefore bathed in this very hot air. The energy transportation mechanism of the boundary layer serves to keep the molecules of air next to the skin highly agitated (at a high random velocity) although they are continually giving up energy as they occasionally come in contact with the skin which is cool relative to this bath of extremely hot air.

In the case of a weak shock wave, the events are different but the results are the same. In this case the weak shock wave may contribute only a small additional random velocity to the air molecules since the relative velocity between air and spacecraft may be only slightly decreased as the air passes through the shock wave. Thus, the air becomes only partially heated in traversing such a shock wave. However, there is then a great difference in velocity across the boundary layer. The exchange of kinetic energy between the various molecules in the boundary layer is sufficient for the high velocity of air flow over the

spacecraft to be transferred into a high random velocity of
the individual molecules at the bottom of the boundary layer.

The nature of the boundary layer activity is such that nearly
the full stagnation temperature will be created at the bottom
of the boundary layer regardless of the shape of the spacecraft. Thus, the air that is adjacent to the skin is at a temperature almost exclusively a function of the forward velocity of
the spacecraft. However, the amount of heat transferred to the
skin is also dependent upon the density of the air in the
boundary layer and upon the degree of scrubbing. *Scrubbing*
is a term used to describe the effectiveness of the boundary
layer to transport energy and momentum into the skin.

Figure 8-10 shows the boundary layer that has formed on
a cone in a wind tunnel test. It can be seen that at the tip of
the cone where the air first comes in contact with the cone's
surface, the boundary layer is extremely thin. It gradually
thickens as the flow progresses over the cone. About half-way
back, the boundary layer can be seen to become suddenly
thicker and slightly unsteady. Up to this point, the boundary
layer is laminar, but it now becomes turbulent. The scrubbing
is extremely severe where the boundary layer is very thin at
the cone tip. As the laminar boundary layer thickens, the
scrubbing becomes less severe. However, when the boundary

Fig. 8-10. Photograph of a cone in a Mach 2 wind tunnel. The
boundary layer can be seen as a thin white layer on the lower side
of the cone. The arrow denotes the point of transition to turbulent
flow. (NASA)

layer changes and becomes turbulent, scrubbing once again becomes severe. This is because in this unsteady condition, portions of high velocity air in the free stream are swept deeply into the boundary layer by the turbulence. This deep mixing greatly assists the transport of momentum and energy from the free stream to the skin. The turbulent boundary layer also thickens and the scrubbing once again becomes less severe further back along the cone. The location on the body at which transition from a laminar boundary layer to a turbulent one occurs depends upon a great many things. The most important is the Reynolds number, which is primarily proportional to size of the body, velocity, and air density.

In the case of a blunt body, the boundary layer flow starts from the stagnation point. Because there is no surface velocity at this point, it is difficult to say that a boundary layer exists. However, as the flow progresses over the surface of the body, the velocity increases and a turbulent boundary layer is formed. Under these conditions, the tendency for the boundary layer to thicken as it travels along the surface is compensated for by the fact that the flow velocity also increases. The net effect is that the severity of scrubbing may either increase

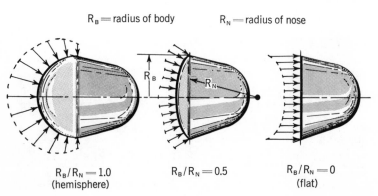

Fig. 8-11.   Effect of nose radius on aerodynamic heating. The lengths of the small arrows indicate the relative degree of heating that the surfaces of these noses would experience if they were exposed to heating by air of identical velocity and density.

or decrease with increased distance from the stagnation point, depending on the bluntness. A flat nose will experience greater heating near the edge than in the center. However, a hemispherical-shaped nose will have its highest heating at the center. A modest amount of curvature on the front surface, such as used by the Mercury vehicle, will result in almost uniform heating across the entire front surface. The boundary layer on a blunt nose may also become turbulent if the Reynolds number is sufficiently large.

The rear portion of a body experiences a negligible amount of heating relative to the forebody. This is because the density is very low in this region at hypersonic velocities. The heating rate on the Mercury afterbody varied from ten percent to less than one percent of the heating on the forebody. Indeed, there were areas on the Mercury spacecraft afterbody where paint was not even scorched.

In general, a blunt body will experience a great deal less heating during the entire reentry period than a slender one. This is a result of several things. The blunt body will expose less forebody surface area to heating. On the other hand, the slender body will be bathed by air moving at a greater velocity and the scrubbing on it will be more severe near the nose. Another important factor favoring the blunt body, is that it has a much greater drag coefficient. This means that a blunt spacecraft of comparable size and weight will decelerate at a higher altitude than will a slender one. Thus, the blunt spacecraft will be exposed to a further reduction in heating since the density of the air that it encounters during its reentry deceleration will be less.

A blunt body is the ideal shape for a reentry vehicle because it dissipates almost all of its kinetic energy by pushing a strong shock wave through the air ahead of itself. Only a very small amount of the kinetic energy of the reentry vehicle is soaked up in the boundary layer. And of the heat introduced in the boundary layer, only a portion gets transferred into the spacecraft structure. This is most fortunate since the spacecraft has an awesome amount of kinetic energy as it plunges toward the atmosphere at the beginning of its reentry. The entire

Mercury spacecraft would have been completely vaporized before it had lost six percent of its velocity, if all the kinetic energy dissipated into the atmosphere had been converted instead into heat within the spacecraft.

Protection Against Reentry Heating

A great deal of heat gets transferred from the boundary to the skin of a spacecraft during reentry. Engineers use three basic schemes to deal with this heat. These are the use of thermal capacity, thermal radiation, and material ablation.

The simplest scheme is to provide enough thermal capacity in the outer structure so that the heat may all be soaked up without melting or otherwise damaging the structure. The trouble with this scheme is that most structural materials have a low heat capacity and would therefore have to be quite heavy. This type of heat protection system is best for heating periods that do not have a long duration. In such cases, an extremely high heating rate may be withstood.

Berylium is the best candidate material for this purpose. It has a specific heat of 0.4 and retains useful structural properties up to about 1500°F.

When the heating periods have an extended duration, but the heating rate is modest, heat may be best disposed of by radiation. In this case, the skin attains a sufficiently high temperature so that all of the heat transferred into the skin from the boundary layer is in turn radiated away. In this case a very thin skin is sufficient. Refractory alloys or metals that are resistant to very high temperatures are ideal for this purpose. Ceramics may also be used, but it is difficult to make a lightweight skin with brittle material. Radiative heat protection schemes are limited to heating rates that produce equilibrium temperatures that will not seriously weaken the skin.

The use of ablative surfaces is often the most practical scheme for heat protection during reentry. Ablative surfaces can withstand both very high heating rates and long periods of heating. The chief drawback is that the ablative material is sacrificed during the reentry, and therefore must be replaced if the spacecraft is to be used again. The weight savings that can be achieved through use of ablative material usually predominates all other considerations.

An ablative skin protects against aerodynamic heating by the combined action of blocking the transfer of heat from the boundary layer, by soaking up some of the heat, and by radiating the remainder. The most common types of ablator become charred during exposure to heat. They are commonly a mixture of glass or quartz fibers, micro-balloons, and some type of polymer. The polymer not only acts as a binder, but plays an important role in the ablative action. It chars when it becomes heated, releasing large quantities of gas and absorbing heat since charring is an endothermic reaction. The gases that are produced flow outward from the surface and tend to form a blanket between the boundary layer and the surface. This greatly reduces the effectiveness of the boundary layer to conduct heat to the surface. This blockage of aerodynamic heating is one of the most important functions of an ablative heat shield. As the binder chars, it leaves a carbonaceous material. This material is a very effective radiator of heat since it may attain extremely high surface temperatures. Most of the heat that penetrates the blocking action of the ablation gases is shed by radiation. The remainder soaks into the material and is absorbed either by raising the temperature of the material or by pyrolizing (charring) the polymer.

The glass or quartz fibers give the material strength. When sufficiently heated, however, they melt and partially vaporize, thereby assisting in the ablation action.

It is common practice to bond the ablation material to either a metal or fiberglass structural skin. It is important that the bond between the ablative material and the sub-structure remain intact during the period of reentry heating. Thus, the bond-line must remain below the temperature that the adhesive can withstand. For this reason, an important property for ablative materials to possess is very low thermal conductivity. Otherwise, the bond-line adhesive would fail from overheating before much of the ablative material had been used.

It is for this reason that micro-balloons are sometimes included in the formulations. These are very small, hollow spheres made of plastic or glass. When mixed into the ablative material, they greatly reduce the density and lower the heat conductivity. By lowering the density, the distance the heat must travel to reach the bond-line is increased (for a given weight of ablative material). This factor, in conjunction with the lowered heat conductivity, make the micro-balloons very effective in maintaining a low bond-line temperature.

A typical section through the skin of a spacecraft protected with ablative material is shown in Figure 8-12. This figure illustrates the more important actions involved during the period of intense heating. A fully established char layer is shown. Immediately below the char layer, pyrolysis of the ablation material is taking place as the char layer deepens. The gases produced by pyrolysis percolate through the char layer and stream out from the surface resisting the action of the boundary layer to carry heat into the surface. Below the area of pyrolysis, the material is in its original condition but is gradually being heated by the conduction of heat from the surface. On the left side of the figure is shown a typical temperature profile. The ablation material is shown to be bonded to a structural skin, which is separated from the inner wall of

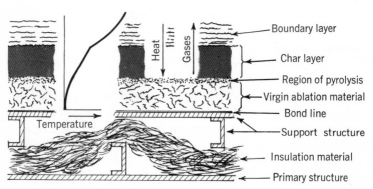

Fig. 8-12.   Action of ablative heat protection.

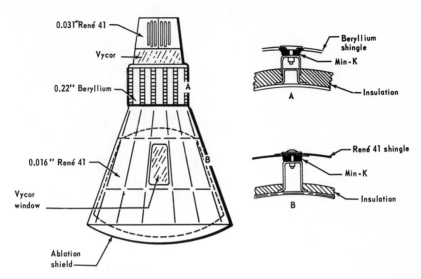

Fig. 8-13. Mercury spacecraft heat protection. (NASA)

the spacecraft by a gap filled with a blanket of insulation material. An arrangement of the type shown is able to maintain the temperature of the inner wall of the cabin to within a few degrees of the initial temperature throughout the reentry period. It will also maintain the primary structure at temperatures within the working range of light weight metals although the outer edge of the char layer may experience temperatures as high as 5000°F.

Figure 8-13 shows the reentry heat protection system carried on the Mercury capsule. All three schemes for heat protection were employed on various areas of the Mercury capsule. The blunt heat shield used an ablation material since this area was exposed to the most intense heating. The conical afterbody was covered with very thin (.016 inch) shingles made of a nickel-cobalt alloy, since in this area the heating rates produced radiation equilibrium temperatures at which this material could be used. The shingles were much lighter per unit-area than the ablation heat shield. On the cylindrical section, a thick berylium shingle was used. In this case, the most severe

Fig. 8-14.   Mercury heat shield after reentry. (NASA)

heating rates would have produced temperatures which would have seriously weakened shingles of the type used on the conical section. On the other hand, the minimum thickness of ablation material that could have been applied would have been heavier than the berylium shingles which were used. The berylium was made thick enough (0.22 inch) to absorb the most severe heat load without exceeding a safe temperature.

The antenna can, which is the small truncated cone at the very top of the capsule, is also made of the nickel-cobalt alloy. However, this portion is 0.06 inch thick. The dielectric material used in the antenna assembly was vicor. The outer panes of the window were also made of vicor, which is a high temperature quartz material.

Landing and Recovery

A manned space mission terminates with the landing of the spacecraft and its subsequent recovery. The landing area for Mercury was a location on the high seas chosen prior to the start of the mission. Both the Apollo and Gemini spacecraft will also use the oceans as their landing area. These spacecraft all use large parachutes to reduce their descent velocity to less than 30 feet per second at water impact. The reason that conventional airplane-like landings were not employed was the result of both operational and engineering factors which strongly favored a water landing and a parachute system. Some of these will be discussed.

The launching of manned spacecraft takes place over the Atlantic Ocean. A failure of the launch vehicles may result in the spacecraft not achieving orbital flight. In this case, it must almost certainly come down in the ocean. Thus, regardless of the location of the planned mission termination point, the spacecraft must be designed to safely negotiate emergency landings in the water. Spacecraft must also be designed for emergency landings on the ground, since an escape maneuver executed near the moment of launch will not carry the spacecraft over the ocean. Thus, the designer must always provide for the possibility of a landing on either the water or the ground.

The parachute is an excellent means to accommodate landing on a wide variety of surfaces. This is because with a parachute, the total velocity at contact can be kept very small. With a horizontal landing maneuver, such as airplanes employ, a very low vertical velocity can be achieved. This makes it possible to execute a very gentle landing on a prepared surface. However, on unprepared terrain, the large horizontal velocity at contact creates the potential of a hazardous landing. Similarly, when "ditching" on the water, the horizontal velocity can cause an airplane to flip over or come apart and sink.

Besides being more suitable for unprepared terrain, the parachute is an ideal descent system for a spacecraft, since it can be compactly stored and therefore imposes only negligible constraints on the spacecraft design. Thus, the shape of the spacecraft can be selected to be quite suitable for launch vehicle and reentry aerodynamics. On the other hand, if a spacecraft must land like a conventional airplane, its shape, which may provide good aerodynamic behavior during the landing maneuver, will be more difficult to carry on the nose of the launch vehicle. It will also have an unnecessarily large amount of surface exposed to the reentry heating environment. The overall effect will be that it may weigh several times as much as the compact spacecraft that employs a parachute for landing.

With a parachute landing system, the use of ocean areas as the normal landing location is ideal. To begin with, the water surface is a good shock absorber. Thus, if water is chosen as the normal landing surface, the shock attenuation system need only be designed for emergency land landings. From a structural standpoint, this means that minor structural damage is acceptable in the improbable circumstance that the spacecraft lands on the ground. From a crew protection standpoint, it means that the shock of a land landing need only be attenuated sufficiently to assure the avoidance of serious injury. Thus, the use of a water landing as the normal mode further enhances the value of a parachute landing system by eliminating some of the weight required for shock attenuation.

From an operational standpoint, a water landing has both good and bad features. The danger of the capsule sinking after landing is undoubtedly the most serious drawback to landing on the water. One of the most misunderstood considerations is that associated with recovery. It is often pointed out that the danger of being lost at sea is a serious drawback to water landing. Actually, the reverse is true. If a spacecraft that is intended to land on the ground is faulty in its return navigation, a much more serious recovery situation may be created. Not only might the spacecraft be temporarily lost, but the subsequent search may have to be carried out over hazardous and difficult terrain. Aggravating the situation would be the likelihood that the spacecraft may have been seriously damaged or destroyed in a rough landing.

There are other considerations that strongly favor the use of open waters for the landing. Ocean landings allow for the selection of a landing area where the population density is extremely small. While it is unlikely that a descending spacecraft will ever injure anyone on the ground, the ocean areas are an excellent way to avoid unnecessary hazards of this type. A further consideration is that when spacecraft become more

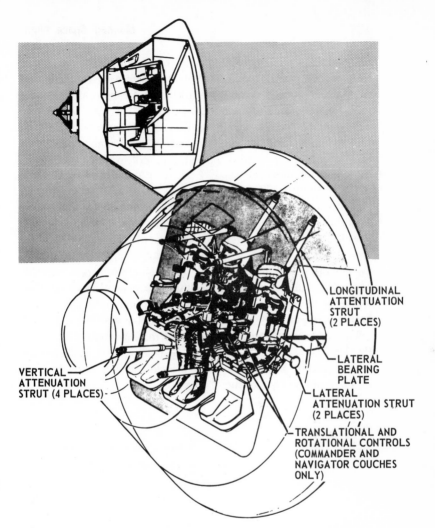

Fig. 8-15. Impact attenuation system for Apollo crew couches. (NASA)

sophisticated, they probably will jettison heavier pieces of unnecessary equipment just prior to reentry. The Mercury spacecraft jettisoned its retro-rockets, Gemini will jettison a large section of its adaptor, and Apollo will jettison a service module that is heavier than the reentry capsule. These pieces must all be accounted for after they are jettisoned, and a calculation of their predicted path must show that they do not impact near populated areas. Since these pieces are following nearly the same initial trajectory as the reentering capsule, they will normally come down near it. While the lifting capability of the spacecraft can be used to separate its landing point from that of the jettisoned equipment, such a maneuver may result in a serious operational constraint that would otherwise be unnecessary.

While the present state of technology strongly points to continued use of the ocean areas for spacecraft landing, the future is not always easy to predict. There is a considerable effort to develop suitable systems to make a land landing more desirable and practical. Gliding parachutes have already been developed which would combine many of the good features of a glider and a parachute. However, it would appear that water landing systems will always be lighter in weight. Thus, high performance spacecraft (those that carry out the most advanced exploration missions) will most probably return to the Earth's oceans. When returning from planetary distances, who would quibble about using a little Earth-type transportation to complete his journey home?

Bibliography

Coombs, Charles, *Project Apollo—Mission to the Moon*. New York: Morrow, 1965, 96 pp.

A‑simple explanation of the proposed three-man journey to the moon—from launching to return to earth—written in graphic style as though the flight were actually under way. (Gr. 5–8)

Hines, William, *Conquest of the Moon*. New York: Pyramid, 1964, 160 pp.

An account of America's preparations for sending a manned mission to the moon, based on facts gathered from NASA and the aerospace industry. (Gr. 9–12, adult)

Morganthaler, Geo. W., and Horace, Jacobs (co-editors), *Manned Lunar Flight*. California: Western Periodicals Co.

National Aeronautics and Space Administration, *Mercury Project Summary*. Washington, D. C.: Superintendent of Documents, Government Printing Office.

Purser, Faget, and Smith, *Manned Space Craft, Engineering Design and Operation*. New York: Fairchild Publications, Inc.

Scharff, Robert, *Into Space with the Astronauts*. New York: Grosset, 1965, 48 pp.

How an astronaut is trained to fly in space. Discusses the hazards of space flight and how they will be overcome. Explains space terms and describes the accomplishment of manned space flights and plans for reaching the moon. (Gr. 6–8)

Shankle, Ralph, *The Twins of Space*. Pennsylvania: Lippincott, 1964, 223 pp.

A report on Project Gemini—the Gemini astronauts and their training, the Gemini spacecraft, and the hoped-for accomplishments of Gemini missions. (Gr. 9–12, adult)

Stambler, Irwin, *Project Gemini*. New York: Putnam, 1964, 64 pp.

An explanation of Project Gemini, the successor to Project Mercury, and our next step toward the moon. How the project differs from other U.S. and Russian space programs, what it hopes to accomplish, and how it will add to our ability to reach the moon. (Gr. 7–12, adult)

Index